THE

SAND

BUCKET

LIST

Lessons for Living Life and Facing Death

BRAD FISCHER

CONTENTS

INTRODUCTION

ON JUNE 14, 2018, AT the age of forty-six, I was diagnosed with *poorly differentiated adenocarcinoma*, a highly aggressive cancer with a poor prognosis that was first detected in my stomach. My first round of chemotherapy began the following month. I was warned about some of the side effects of chemo. My oncologist informed me that I might feel nauseous. I did, but thanks to anti-nausea medicine, that was manageable. He said it might take away my energy. I was more tired than normal, but that too wasn't as bad as I had anticipated. He said most people become sensitive to cold things. He was right. Grabbing a carton of milk felt like I had submerged my wrist in a bowl of ice water, and drinking a glass of cold water felt like swallowing shards of glass. But I quickly became accustomed to wearing oven mitts to handle anything inside the refrigerator and learned to take only small sips of room-temperature liquids.

What I wasn't prepared for—and what I hated the most—was not *something* in particular that I felt. It was *everything* that I felt. And everything I *didn't* feel. The drug Oxaliplatin in the chemotherapy had a way of making all stimuli overwhelming. When trying to read a book, the words danced across the pages, scrambling all meaning. Watching TV felt like someone was flashing a strobe light and banging cymbals next to my head. Audiobooks I had been eager to listen to were incoherent and annoying. Hearing my kids tell me about their day felt like someone was shouting at me in a foreign language. I wanted to close my eyes in a quiet room and remove myself from all sensation. I wasn't angry. I wasn't sad. I wasn't in pain. I didn't even feel terribly sick. I was numb. And I wanted to stay numb. I was a shell of a human who wanted to feel absolutely nothing.

Fortunately, the side effects did get better. My treatment was also adjusted and became easier to tolerate. But even after being off chemo for almost a year, I still had some of the side effects, such as numbness and a tingling sensation in both my feet—similar to what it feels like when you have an extremity that "goes to sleep." Doctors called it neuropathy. I called it "freaky feet" and accepted it as some of my collateral damage that comes with survival. There was a benefit of freaky feet. It was a regular reminder of that awful feeling of numbness I felt when taking chemo. They were my daily reminder to be thankful for life. To enjoy life. To live life. To *feel* life.

When I learned that the average survival period for my stage and form of cancer was about twelve months, I reflected on my life and faced my own mortality. I realized all the things I hadn't done. I had never gone bungee jumping, skydiving, or ridden in a hot air balloon.

I had not run a marathon or ridden a mechanical bull. I had only seen a very small fraction of the countries in the world, had never been to the Olympic games, hadn't seen the movie *The Godfather*, and had never eaten a fried tarantula.

There is so much I still wanted to do. That I needed to do.

After I surpassed the twelve-month life expectancy, my family, some close friends, and I decided to celebrate and soak in the sun—and life— with a vacation to Fort Walton Beach in Florida. The view was beautiful, the company fantastic, the weather perfect. We spent a good portion of our time sitting in chairs along the beach and digging holes in the sand for the kids—only to fill them again at the end of the day. Although every- thing about the experience was wonderful, I couldn't help but think, *What am I doing?* Or, more precisely, *What am I not doing? Is this living?*

My time felt precious. I felt fortunate to be lying on a beach feeling normal again. After all, normalcy was what I craved the most. But as I sat in a beach chair watching two of my friends dig craters in the sand, I couldn't help but think, *Surely there's more to my life than this?* Was I spared and given more time on Earth so I could watch two grown men shove a plastic shovel into the sand?

I restlessly asked myself, *How should I be spending my time?* I had always taken pride in my ability to prioritize and compartmentalize. At work and in my personal life, I always had more on my daily to-do list than I could possibly get done. Juggling multiple projects, responsibil- ities, and even "emergencies" was part of what I loved about the job and even some of the twisted joy of parenting. But after my diagnosis, suddenly everything in my life had a way of seeming both meaningful and meaningless at the same time.

Everything felt urgent, but nothing obtainable. When I thought I had less than a year to live, I told myself I wanted to make my family the priority. But what did that mean exactly—especially when it came to deciding how to spend my time? Should I work as much as possible while I am physically able to help reduce the financial burden that they could face when my health deteriorates? Should I focus on getting my funeral/burial arrangements in order? Should I focus on simply being present for my wife, Tonya, and our two girls, Anna Mae and Lizzie—savoring each soccer game, cheerleading event, shared meals, or car rides together? Should I focus on writing—to give my kids something to guide them in their own life journey after I am gone? Should I focus on the daily chores—helping with laundry, cleaning, cooking—because those things don't just help make our home feel normal, they make our lives feel normal? Or should I focus on building memories with my family, committing to more vacations, trips, and time together?

Everything that stood in front of me seemed absolutely essential and completely trivial at the same time. I felt restless and ridiculous digging a hole on the beach, yet the task felt critical to living a complete life because it hinted at building a happy memory with my kids. I felt perfectly healthy and capable of digging the hole, yet I wondered if my corpse soon would be lying in a similarly sized hole. Finding myself somewhere between being cured and dead had given me enough hope to believe that I still could get everything checked off my list, but with the keen awareness of the limited time I had left to do them.

Not only had I not checked off everything on some bucket list, I hadn't even taken the time to *create* a bucket list. Perhaps that was why I felt both overwhelmed and restless at the same time. Perhaps a bucket list would help me prioritize my time.

So, I started to brainstorm ideas of things I must see or do before I die. It was tempting to gravitate to some of the most popular ideas, which seemed to be a combination of adventure and travel. After all, most of the ideas sounded interesting and fun. Who wouldn't want to dive the Great Barrier Reef or ride a camel in Israel? Others were definitely outside my comfort zone, but certainly would evoke strong feelings: Riding a mechanical bull, going to a nude beach, or visiting an active war zone may all be events that make me *feel* something, but even if I rode a mechanical bull naked in Afghanistan, I'm not sure I would feel more accomplished and my life would seem more complete.

As angry as I was (and perhaps still am) at what cancer had taken from me, it had a way of magnifying the moments of my life—playing back memories in my mind in slow motion. What I realized is that it's not *what* I'm doing that has mattered most, it's *who* I'm doing it with and *why* I'm doing it. (Why travel? Why jump out of an airplane? Why ride a mechanical bull? Why dig and fill a hole on the beach?) The worth of anything I had done in my life almost always came back to how it made others feel. When people around me were laughing, I felt happier. If I helped overcome a problem or challenge that others were facing, I felt like I learned something. When I helped others feel more loved, I felt more loved.

The secret to leading a meaningful, fulfilling life became clear to me: I didn't need a bucket list. Instead, my life's most precious moments have consisted of three simple ingredients: laughter, learning, and love. In other words, what has given me purpose and meaning in life isn't some bucket list, a collection of arbitrary adventures I wanted to do *once* in my life. Instead, what has given me purpose is focusing on those things in my life I wanted to do as *frequently* and *thoroughly* as possible. Like a simple, plastic bucket that can be used to create beautiful sandcastles on the shore by packing fine sand with the right amount of water and imagination, I wanted to create beauty in—and from—my life by packing it with laughter, learning, and love.

This book is about the lessons I learned both through living life and facing death. I haven't lived a perfect life or even a completely fulfilled life, but I have led a fulfilling life. I hope my lessons can help guide my two daughters as they become adults, comfort families that have been touched by cancer or who face any form of suffering, and inspire those searching for meaning in the ragged routines of life. This is for anyone who feels like they are digging holes on the beach only to fill them back in later. I hope my stories give you strength, a laugh, and perspective on your own life. I hope they give you a voice to share your own stories and become a catalyst for you to live the life you want to lead.

This book isn't about dying, nor a story about fighting cancer. It's a book about life. It's a book about living.

SECTION 1

LAUGH

"A day without laughter is a day wasted."

– CHARLIE CHAPLIN

THE BEST MOMENTS OF MY life almost always included laughter. It doesn't often take a lot for me to laugh. The hardest times I laughed didn't require a professional comedian or anyone finding my secret tickle spots. It typically involved a few of my friends and something that happened that was insignificant, stupid and yet utterly hilarious.

I want to...

- ❖ Be with people who make me laugh.
- ❖ Go places that make me laugh.
- ❖ Do things that make me laugh.
- ❖ Help make others laugh.

Examples of things that make me laugh...

- ❖ Hearing my wife regularly mix her idioms and say bewildering things like "It isn't rocket surgery!"
- ❖ Squirting my kids with water on the last day of school.
- ❖ Watching my friends and complete strangers transform into a bull on the dance floor while I serve the role as their matador.

CHAPTER 1:

CAT SORES

Life Lesson: *Even when you're "feline" bad,*
don't let anyone or anything define you.

The word "cancer" isn't a label for me. That is a title for others. The first time I heard the word as a kid, I thought of it as an ailment that attacks grandparents. I was told it was the thief that took the life of my grandfather, Arthur Grundhoefer (my mother's dad) at the age of fifty-nine, before I was born, leaving me only with stories of the warm, loving man who my mom assured me would have laughed at my jokes and been at all my sporting events. It was the reason a lot of my friends no longer had their grandparents either.

Still as a child, my awareness of the disease broadened and I realized *cancer* was the villain that made my Uncle Dan carry his own feces in a bag, because it thinks that sort of thing is funny, I supposed. But apparently, that kind of humor only gets a laugh for a short while, because it ultimately decided that taking his life with a different form of cancer must make for a better punchline. Cancer felt so comfortable in Dan's home that it decided to crash into the lives of my mom's other siblings, taking up a dedicated room with five other uncles, an aunt, and five of my first cousins, snuffing out the lives of four of its victims.

Cancer is also the intruder that bit my brother and my sister-in-law. It was the faceless beast that entered the brain of my nephew Paul at the age of nine, chewing at his body for a couple of years until it also extinguished the life of this witty, caring, giving, smart, playful boy who loved football, family, God, and life.

Cancer is the scoundrel who cheated its way into the lives of my classmates, colleagues, my friends, people I loved, people I really didn't like, and people I didn't know. So, I knew the title of cancer wasn't just a label for old people, smokers, or people who deserved it. It doesn't discriminate. It really doesn't care. It wants to crash into as many bodies and homes as possible.

Although I would wear colorful ribbons, throw change in the box in the McDonald's drive-through, walk for a cause, donate money, help my kids sell cookies and crafts for the local hospital, say prayers for others, grieve for others, and see the width and depth of its reach, I was pretty confident cancer wasn't going to get me. I was going to trick it. Through exercise, eating right, saying my prayers, and being thankful, I'd show it and the world that I was too slippery for cancer to attach itself to me. I was Teflon to this greasy disease.

That plan worked perfectly—until it didn't. Indiscriminately, I was handed the same label and asked to display it on my chest for others to see. It welcomed me into its membership with little warning, trial period, or money-back guarantee. In an instant, I was a card-holding lifetime member of the cancer club. There had been no initiation. I wasn't given a ring of commitment or a vow of solidarity.

But I knew cancer's history and the way it treats others within its reach. Although I knew it wasn't monogamous in its relationships, it remained a committed companion to everyone it touches. Even those who have found a way to kick it out of their house and keep their doors locked at night know it might crash through their windows any time it pleases.

The messenger for me was the intelligent, talented, world-renowned gastroenterologist, Dr. Douglas Rex, at Indiana University Health Hospital. Because he dedicates most of his life to scoping patients, he probably holds a stack of cards with the "cancer" label pre-printed, ready to hand out to his next visitor. I could tell he felt empathy when he handed me the card and explained my diagnosis, but his solemn look only made me want to reject the card even more. Nevertheless, the card with the "C word" printed in a big bold font came home with me, made my wife instantly feel sorrow when she looked at me, caused confusion among my eleven- and thirteen-year-old daughters, and became a footnote everywhere my name was spoken.

But that's not me. Really! THAT IS NOT ME! I'm more than that. I'm the guy whose dance moves are still waiting to become popular, the goofball who thinks cows are funny, and the person who invented the smallest jack-o'-lantern contest but then felt too busy to participate in the competition. I'm the friend who came up with the name Scared Hitless for our volleyball team and your buddy who wants to drink a beer in your man shed and pretend I'm up to date on the latest draft picks. I'm the colleague who wants to show you a cool spreadsheet formula and the boss who makes every new idea an alliteration. I'm the sibling who played rubber monkeys with you and the son borrowing a fishing pole on your boat who has been warned repeatedly not to talk politics. I'm the dad who squirts you with water on the last day of school and the husband who forgets to transfer the laundry from the washer to the dryer.

I'm all of those things and so much more. I'm not the guy with cancer.

At least that's what I told myself. In fact, instead of accepting that label, I tried to replay and even remake the conversation when Dr. Rex delivered the news. Only this time, I changed the scene completely. Instead of a cold, sterile office hospital, I imagined he and I were at a bar with the vibration of the loud music shaking the beer in our glasses.

Dr. Rex is laughing at me imitating a dinosaur—which, incidentally, is another strength of mine—mocking the name D. Rex because of its similarities to T. Rex. In my fantasy, D. Rex and I are having a good time. But then his expression changes to a sorrowful gaze. Without any warning, he changes the conversation and with a look of misery in his eyes he delivers the ominous news: "Brad, you have cancer."

But over the loud music and my attention deafened by a few drinks, I shout back, "How the hell did I get cat sores?"

He laughs for a second, then regains his solemn look. The conversation continues. We both cry a little, then laugh again at my misunderstanding and genuine stupidity. He goes back to cheering me on, so I start acting like a dinosaur again, and we both forget for an instant that the sentence had ever been muttered. And, for a moment, things feel normal again.

Normal. I wanted to feel normal again. So, I decided that I would have cat sores instead—because living with cancer was too scary. That was simply not a label for me.

The word "cancer" would cause people to gasp, grimace, or give me a sorrowful gaze. I feared the disease, but I hated the doom and darkness that it brought to everyone I loved. So, I insisted others call it cat sores—as if some fictitious story of stomping around in a bar like a dinosaur would safeguard both myself and those around me from the seriousness of my situation. Even if I couldn't beat it, I wanted to pretend that I could—not only for myself, but for my friends, my wife, and my daughters.

I also found some dark humor with calling my condition "cat sores." I would run into people I knew well who understandably didn't know whether or not to bring up my new reality. Evoking the word "cancer" felt like inviting the grim reaper to the conversation. So, we talked about cat sores instead, simply some annoying ailment. I also chuckled to myself picturing people hearing and then spreading the news to mutual friends with solemn statements like "Did you hear that Brad has cat sores?"

All my inboxes were quickly filled with a rallying cry to defeat cat sores. Comforting cards, spiritual outreaches, inspiring words, and supportive hands reached me with a slice of my own humor, the words "cat sores" interwoven in each message. The love was nearly overwhelming. The love kept me moving forward. It gave me peace knowing that there were others willing to help my family as our journey on this dark and winding path was just beginning. But laughter allowed me to feel a bit of normalcy—even when everything around me was crumbling.

We are praying for your complete healing of cat sores. Messages like these offered me hope and comic relief. I wondered if God shared my sense of humor. I was about to find out.

CHAPTER 2:

BROKEN

Life Lesson: Broken crayons still color,
so keep adding color to life.

EVEN THOUGH CALLING MY DIAGNOSIS "cat sores" added some needed comic relief, I couldn't escape the weight of the truth. And, the truth was that the diagnosis didn't involve drinks, a band, and my dinosaur impersonation, and my prognosis was no laughing matter. The truth is that cat sores made me feel broken.

My symptoms had started three or four months prior, something I hadn't fully admitted to myself. I told myself that the pain in my stomach must be from something that I'd eaten or perhaps, at worst, was an ulcer that would heal eventually. The sensation wasn't a piercing pain—just a dull ache that didn't seem to go away and kept getting worse. I also had the odd sensation of feeling like I needed to belch frequently, especially after drinking anything. I blamed it on some of my bad habits. I started each morning with a couple cups of coffee and would frequently skip breakfast. I thought my body was rebelling against me drinking caffeine on an empty stomach in the morning—or perhaps was finally getting even with me for poisoning it with overdoses of Busch Light and Taco Bell when I was twenty-five years younger.

But after allowing the pain to continue for a few months, I finally reached out to my primary care doctor, who put me on some acid reflux meds. I went through three different prescriptions. None of them helped. During the day, my busy schedule would keep my mind occupied, allowing me to ignore the dull pain. But at night, my mind would settle on the ache in my stomach and would struggle to set the pain to the side. I'd wake up in the middle of the night and find myself groaning—not because the pain was unbearable, but because it continually squeezed at my gut without relief. My primary care doctor thought I needed to give it more time. But since my own trusted method of tending to my health—a Google search—was informing me that I may have an ulcer, I asked to meet with a specialist.

Dr. Douglas Rex already knew me pretty well. In fact, he knew parts of me better than anyone, considering he had seen the inside of my colon multiple times. He was well aware of my family's history with colon cancer. Some blood work I had done in my early twenties revealed that I also had Lynch syndrome, a genetic mutation that made it much more likely for me to develop colon cancer. Because of that increased risk, every two years I made my appointment with Dr. Rex to "change my oil"—just one of my many expressions for having a colonoscopy. I had seen him only a year ago for my routine colonoscopy; two years prior to that, he gave me the "GI works"—a colonoscopy and endoscopy. Both procedures came back clear and had me back on the road until my next 3,000-mile tune-up.

When I met with him this time, in addition to sharing my symptoms, I thought I'd skip a few steps and ask if he could offer anything to help with an ulcer. Apparently, my self-diagnosis from a two-minute Google search wasn't convincing to him, because he wanted to do another endoscopy. It seemed excessive to me. I hoped for a simple prescription, perhaps some advice on what to eat, and the typical approach of "keeping an eye on it." But since I had grown tired of living with the pain in my gut, I reluctantly decided to take a day off work to have the procedure. I would be sedated, so my wife, Tonya, tagged along as my driver.

The plan seemed pretty straightforward in my mind. An anesthesiologist would put me out, Dr. Rex would do his thing, confirm my suspicion of having an ulcer, give me some healing meds, I'd schedule my next tune-up, and I'd be on my way to feeling normal again by the next morning.

But this time was different. I awoke to the solemn face of Dr. Rex with Tonya sitting by my side. He looked at us both and said matter-of-factly, pointing to images he held in his hand, "I found this abnormal tissue on the lining of your stomach."

Tonya reached for my hand and I found myself squeezing it.

He continued, "It's a mass that's poorly defined." He went into detail about the makeup, size, and location, then looked at both of us with a sorrowful gaze and pointedly added: "It's cancer."

My senses grew numb. Surely I was still in a deep sleep from the anesthesia and this was all a nightmare.

The day continued with more tests—including a PET/CT scan and endoscopic ultrasound. Although they would have to wait a couple days for reports from the biopsy about some of the specifics, the conclusion was already formed. It was cancer. It looked like it had already spread throughout my lymph nodes—and if that were the case, it would already be considered stage 4. Although I didn't know a lot about the classifications of cancer, I had never heard of a stage 5.

As Dr. Rex explained what the additional tests showed, I tried to push away my emotions and focus on a plan. "So what's next?" I said as if this was another project for work with a list of tasks needing completed in some carefully arranged sequence.

He explained that he might suggest removing my stomach. But when I pressed him on that—noting that it appeared to have already spread—he acknowledged the difficult situation by saying, "We are going to do everything we can, and I'm going to need help on this one."

Driving home that day, my mind bounced between unanswered questions. Was there something I might have done to cause this? How long has the tumor been there? Isn't the expression "doing everything we can" really code for there's not much more that we can do? How long do I have left? But my mind settled on the more pressing and practical question: What should I tell our girls, thirteen-year-old Anna Mae, and Lizzie, whose eleventh birthday was only a week away?

First, I needed to be honest with myself. I needed to face the reality of the report I held in my hand. I needed to begin prioritizing my time differently. It was only a matter of time that I would be gone.

It's not my life that flashed before my eyes—it was my girls' lives. Their future also suddenly seemed less clear to me. I hated the thought of not being there for them. I wouldn't be there to watch Lizzie play soccer or watch Anna Mae cheer. I wouldn't be there to help with homework. To teach them to drive. To talk about boyfriends, to *meet* their boyfriends. I wouldn't be there to tickle the bottom of their feet, to steamroll them, to do my dinosaur impersonation for them. I wouldn't be there to share my silly stories, or to listen to theirs.

And perhaps most importantly: I wouldn't be there to make them laugh. I wouldn't be there to hear them laugh.

Exactly one week after my diagnosis, Tonya and I met with my oncologist, Dr. Paul Helft at IU Health University Hospital. It was a long, emotional week. Everything felt more significant and more fleeting. Every moment became *the last time* I would be able to experience it. It was the last time I'd get to watch Lizzie play soccer. The last time I'd hear Anna Mae sing. The last time I'd see a friend. The last time I would be able to say "good night" to the girls. I tried to hold myself together when talking with the girls, but then I would break down at the smallest of moments when I wasn't with them.

Tonya and I walked into Dr. Helft's office feeling tired, distressed, and fearful. As part of the check-in, a nurse took my vitals and had me step on a scale to get my weight. Only a week prior the scale read 177 lbs. Now, it was 165. The countdown had begun. My deterioration had started.

I looked around the waiting area, noticing the frail body frames and bald heads of others waiting. That would soon be me.

The nurse directed us to a room. I sat in a chair next to Tonya as if I were a visitor, not wanting to assume the role of patient on the exam chair draped with paper. Even though we sat shoulder to shoulder, we were quiet because talking about it made everything only feel more real.

Dr. Helft entered the room with his assistant, Pamela. Both approached us with warm smiles. Immediately, Dr. Helft struck me as smart, professional, honest, hopeful—but above all—kind. He didn't sugarcoat my situation, but he listened to my concerns and questions carefully, explained what he knew, and discussed options. There had been some incredible breakthroughs in cancer research in the last few years and "immunotherapy," a relatively new form of treatment that had been FDA approved, had given some patients incredible results—even causing the cancer to disappear in some rare situations.

He also explained some of the unknowns and risks. Immunotherapy would not be an option unless they could confirm that the cancer in my stomach was related to my genetic mutation associated with Lynch syndrome. And if it was, he did not know if my insurance would cover it. And, without sharing the cost, he said, "There is no amount of bake sales or fundraisers that will even put a dent in the cost of one treatment." He also mentioned that there are life-threatening risks. Sometimes the treatment can cause one's own immune system to attack healthy cells in the body—the liver, lungs, and other organs. But he also empathetically explained that the other options of chemotherapy alone probably would not help much—just slow the growth temporarily.

I tried to push Emotional Brad to the side and summoned Analytical Brad to the occasion. There were no guarantees and no absolutes. There were no great choices, but it was essential that I picked the best among a series of bad options. And the way I saw it, my best shot—really my only shot—hinged on a series of nested if-then statements. *If* my genetic mutation did cause my cancer, *then* I might be able to take a new drug, and *if* that new drug didn't kill me and *if* that new drug worked as well with gastric cancer as it had done with other forms of cancer, *then* I might have a ten percent chance of surviving—not just for a few months, but perhaps for several more years. And, *if* my logic was accurate and this was the best course of treatment, *then* I might be able to convince my insurance to agree. It was a long shot, but it was a shot.

The next month consisted of more doctor appointments, more tests, and a surgery to place a port in my chest for treatment, biopsy tissue from my lymph nodes, and excise a small lesion that had started to form on my rectum. The long-term plan remained unknown. We would need to wait for test results to know if immunotherapy was an option. In the meantime, I would begin chemotherapy—a way to slow the cancer's growth, a way to buy time.

Time. It's what I wanted most. And even though I still felt broken, with each new visit, I also felt something other than a countdown in my head.

Hope.

When sitting in one of the patient rooms waiting on Dr. Helft, I noticed a scribbled message that read: *Broken crayons still color.*

That night, when I hugged Anna Mae and Lizzie goodnight, I tickled the bottom of both their feet and savored the moment of hearing their playful laughs. I was a broken crayon. But maybe I could continue to add color to this world for a little longer.

CHAPTER 3:

SHIT PURSE

Life Lesson: *You get what you get,*
but throw out a bag of shit.

WHEN I WAS YOUNG, MY friends and I often played the game of Shit Purse. In case you have not had the same worldly upbringing that I did in the hills of southern Indiana and are not familiar with this particular outdoor activity, allow me to outline the fundamentals. To begin, you need two ingredients: some freshly produced manure from the nearest farm animal and secondly...yep, you guessed it, a purse—preferably one that you are no longer wanting to use.

The preparation phase is pretty straightforward: Insert the manure into the purse. This usually works best if you have a team of two people—one to hold the purse and one to do the shoveling. (Insider tip: The role of shoveler doesn't stink quite as bad—literally—as the role of purse holder.) Close the purse and make it look as presentable as possible. Place the purse on a road and hide, waiting for the comedy to begin.

There are four objectives to the game: 1) to have the purse picked up by an unknowing participant, 2) to have that purse make its way into a vehicle, 3) to have the purse tossed back out the window. And, perhaps most importantly, 4) to witness objectives 1-3 without getting caught.

I'm not sure who invented the game. I'd like to claim credit, but the Shit Purse Master who introduced me to the pastime was my friend Craig. Craig became my professor and mentor for the game probably around fifth grade. And boy was he good at it! First, he had the perfect setup. He lived on a farm with some cows, a few pigs, and thousands of turkeys. Ingredient #1 was in plenty of supply. Secondly, he had a lot of older sisters. I'm not sure if they were always willing participants in this game, but anytime we wanted to play, Craig would disappear in their old farmhouse to some of the upstairs bedrooms and return with his clenched fist above his head, holding the purse like a trophy. Craig also had a mini bike, a motorized vehicle that made our delivery of the goods much more efficient and effective.

Our normal drop-off spot was a busy highway that ran in front of Craig's family farm. The steady traffic made it an optimal location, although the 55 mph speed limit sometimes made it difficult for drivers to detect the foreign object in the middle of their path. We strategically placed the purse about two hundred yards before his driveway to provide our victim a place to turn around in order to get the purse. We would hide on top of a steep hill covered in the grass that overlooked the highway.

Craig did the dirty work—and I don't just mean completing the preparation of the package. He also served as the delivery person for our special gift. My role was a lookout, waiting for the passage to be clear of traffic and give the signal for Craig to execute Operation Shit Purse. Upon my signal, Craig would race down the tall hill to the highway. Like a trained CIA operative making a top-secret drop, Craig would barely slow down, release the purse onto the middle of the highway, then return to the hiding spot with the other conspirators of the game.

Then we waited.

With each vehicle that approached the purse, we lifted our heads above the grasses, watching in anticipation of a stop. Sometimes we waited for hours—or at least it felt that way—as we watched one car after another ignore our bait.

But then it would happen. The red brake lights of the car zooming past the purse would light up. We watched with exhilaration to see the vehicle turn off the highway into Craig's driveway, exactly like we had hoped. Although we wanted to start our pregame fist bumps, we knew to remain still to avoid being detected. Our curiosity could reveal our identity and ruin the game.

We persistently achieved all four objectives of Shit Purse. Although we took great joy in seeing a stranger beside the road inspect the purse's contents, that usually resulted in the purse being dropped immediately. Sure, it made for a good laugh, but we knew the ultimate goal was for the purse to make its way *into* the car and then *out of* the car. Occasionally, a person would grab the purse and jump back into the car—but instead of the purse shooting out of the window moments later, it remained inside the vehicle and we helplessly watched the car drive away with our prized trap, leaving the reaction only to our imaginations. This also had the undesirable effect of ending that round of Shit Purse purse-less, requiring us to snag another purse—and the longer we played this game, the more difficult that became.

So, we longed for that perfect outcome—a result between a premature purse drop and a purse snatch. Ahh, but when it would happen as desired, it was magnificent! The purse would disappear into the vehicle—sometimes, the vehicle would even start to move forward— and then, like a rotten apple core, the purse would come flying out the window and the car would speed away.

We would laugh, celebrate, and laugh more. Not only had we scored in achieving our four objectives, but the purse, still in our possession, was intact and properly prepared for round two. And then the game would continue, with us hiding and cheering at the sight of our foul-smelling purse being tossed out the window of another stranger's vehicle. Shit Purse was the gift that kept on giving.

Cancer had become my shit purse. Its stench clung to everything around it. The disease caused my body's cells to divide without stopping and was eager to attack surrounding tissues. It was found in my stomach, but I knew that it wouldn't be content there; it wanted to find a home in all parts of my anatomy. I hated it. Not only because it's a disease that attacked my body, but it's a filth that wanted to contaminate everything about me and all that surrounded me—my family, my job, my friends, my finances, my thoughts, my personality, my time, my interests, the way people view me, what I like to eat, how I spend my time, and what I do for fun.

The whole situation stunk. Literally. The chemicals used in my treatment had a distinctive smell. My first round of chemotherapy started on July 20, which also happened to be my wedding anniversary. Tonya, my bride of sixteen years, sat next to me as the nurses connected a bag of chemicals to a port in my chest. As the drips poured into my bloodstream, I waited for the poison to transform me—imagining myself growing a tail.

I'm not sure if it was the smell of the medicine being pumped into my body or the chemicals used to clean the infusion equipment, but the odor repulsed me. Even by the time I arrived home, the transformation was beginning. Everything I ate had the taste of metal; cold water felt like it cut my throat as I swallowed. The toxins became the first thing I smelled when waking in the morning, and I would press my nose into my pillow at night hoping to find a moment of not smelling it so I could sleep. It was the smell of sickness, the smell of a foreign substance that wasn't supposed to be in my body, but was there nonetheless to do its part. It was the smell of cancer. The smell of death. A stench that made me gag.

Much like the people in the cars who stopped for the purse in our childish game, I felt cheated. I didn't do anything to deserve this bag of filth. I never smoked. I regularly exercised. I ate healthy food. I had preventive colonoscopies and cancer screenings every two years. I tried to live a good life and treat people with dignity and respect.

And yet, there I sat with a bag of crap in my lap.

As I reflected on my situation and my childhood game of Shit Purse, I realized that the people who became the target in our twisted game also didn't deserve what they received. Those who stopped weren't bad, greedy people who wanted to pocket a few easy bucks. They were probably kind, thoughtful people who wanted to do what was right and help someone. They probably stopped to grab a purse in an attempt to return the personal items, money, and more importantly, the identity of a person they had never met.

But now, I felt like the victim. I wanted my identity back. I was angry. I felt sorry for myself—something that felt weak to admit. I had braced myself for pain. I told myself I had to be tougher than cancer. I could be pretty stubborn, so I thought I could break down physical aches with mental toughness. What I wasn't ready to battle was the feeling of weakness.

Chemo made me feel brittle. Nauseous. Dizzy. Breakable. Like I was made of porcelain. I thought I could be tough, but there I sat struggling to sip my soup.

But I also knew better. My friend Craig didn't just teach me about the game of Shit Purse, he taught me about persistence. When he was only five years old, Craig lost his father in a tragic car accident. In an instant, the man who ran the family farm, the guy who embraced hard work and helping others, the person who was Craig's superhero was gone. But Craig and his mom and siblings never seemed to quit—even though everyone would have understood their desire to do so. They not only kept the family farm, but also, little by little, grew it into something that made them all proud. Craig even started his own successful trucking business and perhaps most importantly, became a superhero to his own family.

So, although I sat with a bag of crap in my lap, I also reminded myself I'm not the one inside the bag. I still held the bag. Although I wouldn't be able to control what cancer did to my body, I could control how I let this bag define me. Some of the baggage that came with cancer would make its way into my house and much of its ugliness was inescapable—I knew that. But I told myself that I still get to choose how I talk about it with others. I may not get to control my destination, but I get to affect those who are with me on this journey. I could try to stay true to the person I was and wanted to be. I could surround myself with people who loved me and I could use my time—however long or short that may be—to let others know how much I loved them. And maybe, with the support and love of others, I could make the scent of this disease into something a little less offensive. Despite what cancer could do to me, maybe I could still be the one to get the last laugh.

Cancer had found its way into my life—and I knew that cancer may even dictate the length of my life. But I refused to let it take control of everything *in* my life. I decided that I would get to control some of that. I would simply choose to toss much of what comes with this awful disease out the window.

CHAPTER 4:

MONKEY & GEORGE

Life Lesson: Family is forever, so you might as well start laughing together.

I GREW UP FILTHY RICH as the youngest of four children. My siblings Kristi, Mark, and Jay and I had it all: pool, basketball court, baseball diamond, collectible cars, and regular attendance to musical concerts. The plastic pool was only four feet in diameter, but crowding in that oasis on a hot summer day as young kids felt more refreshing than the fancy pools at the finest resorts. The basketball court was a rock driveway with a hoop hung from our garage, but when Jay and I faced off against Mark, there wasn't any NBA game more intense. Since our front yard doubled as our baseball diamond, we were required to play around a few trees, a hill, and a ditch that served as our home run fence, but the day I hit a ball over that ditch for the first time, not even Carlton Fisk's walk-off homer could compare. My matchbox car collection wasn't nearly as new or numerous as most kids', but when I pulled the cars out of their protective little case, they were faster than any records by Mario Andretti. The musical concerts that Kristi, Mark, Jay, and I practiced and then performed for Mom and Dad (often with instruments like popcorn in a plastic container) were sold out every time.

Kristi and Mark were the leaders on most activities, assigning Jay and me parts without really much discussion. If we were going to create a song, Kristi would decide what instrument I would play. If we were going to pretend to be professional wrestlers, Mark was clear on whether Jay and I would be the good guy or the bad guy and decide which of us would win or lose in our brawl. We were grateful to be able to design and pick out our own costumes, which usually involved some old robe that made us feel like professionals.

But when Mark was busy playing imaginary baseball by himself (a game that involved no ball but two full teams consisting entirely of invisible players) or when Kristi was busy making up dance steps to Shaun Cassidy's music, Jay and I would bring out our action heroes: Monkey and George. To most unimaginative adults and most short-minded children, Monkey and George were two tiny rubber monkeys that stood about six inches in height. At a glance, they were unimpressive goofy-looking characters that probably would be overpriced even if they sold at the local dime store. They weren't as elaborate as the transformers that could take different shapes, and they couldn't be found in the aisle of Walmart next to all the GI Joe characters or Star Wars figures my friends had collected. To the average human, they were two plain, rather boring, ridiculous-looking rubber monkeys that might capture a toddler's attention for ten minutes.

But Jay and I knew better. We had discovered—no—we had

unleashed their power. They were no ordinary monkeys. They were incredibly versatile athletes—so gifted that they could easily dunk over the top of a lanky Mickey Mouse that stood twice their height. They were fearless army men and members of an elite special operations unit that were called to duty even when an entire city was near collapse by villainous rubber Santa Clauses that could not be killed from the gunfire of an entire platoon of army men. They were boxers, baseball players, tennis players, skydivers, professional divers, race car drivers, rock stars, tightrope walkers, scuba divers, and much more. We had played with them as young kids and continued to play with them through middle school. And, had it not been for the stigma that came with staying home from dates to play with rubber monkeys, Jay and I still might be in Mom and Dad's house today playing with them. We played with them so much that their wires had become flimsy and brittle. But their compound fractures—the wire poking out their arms and legs—just meant they would wear some masking tape as their splint, making them look even tougher, along with the cloak that we had created for them from an old handkerchief.

Financially, our parents always provided for us. My dad worked for the local telephone company. When I was little, my mom stayed at home with me, but when I was eleven or twelve, she went to work at a local factory helping sew the fabric and cushions on chairs. I know money was tight at times when all four of us were little, but they always found a way to get what we needed (not necessarily everything we wanted).

Dad was also constantly inventing contraptions and had his

occasional entrepreneurial experiment. In an effort to teach us how to invest and grow our money, he pitched and sold us on the idea of putting our allowance money into building our own worm farm. It seemed like pretty easy money. The plan was simple: We would buy some worms, throw them in some dirt, add some leaves inside a container, play a little Marvin Gaye, and two or three weeks later we'd have more worms, which we could sell to the local bait shop. So, with our allowance as the seed money, Dad bought the starter worms, tossed in some dirt in an old whiskey barrel that had been cut in half, added a little hog manure to make it really rich, and we waited for the worm orgy to begin.

After a couple weeks, we checked on the worms. We approached the wooden barrel eager to see more critters crawling in the soil, but instead were greeted with the stench of fermenting manure and the horrific sight of the skeletons of all our worms—shriveled, dried, dead. Although no formal necropsy was performed, the general consensus was that the cause of death was an overdose of hog shit.

I was often dirty from things like disassembling worm farms, and nobody could deny that the scent from that worm farm certainly was rich—but that's not why I considered myself filthy rich. I hit the jackpot because life was a daily adventure rooted in love, a slice of learning, and lots of laughter. No one in our family took themselves too seriously, and we were always creating the next adventure that would cause us to laugh, cheer, and celebrate together. Still to this day, we discuss the lessons learned from our failed worm farm, reminisce about the games we invented, and occasionally dream about another mission that only Monkey and George could complete.

As my siblings and I began having our own kids, that bond only grew wider and deeper. The laughter, learning, and love extended to a total of eight grandkids—my two kids plus six of my nieces and nephews. We passed on some of our traditions, like an annual Fischer fishing trip and formed new ones, like the "walnut fund"—another one of Dad's investment strategies, which consists of the grandkids picking up walnuts to trade in for some cash. (We are still waiting for the entire stock of walnuts to be ruined by—in a twist of fate—worms.)

Even though we live apart now, my siblings and I are there for each other—not only for the times when we laugh together or to cheer and celebrate good times together. Our bond has also grown stronger because of the hard times. On December 19, 2011, we learned Jay's nine-year old son, Paul, was diagnosed with a brain tumor, a stage 4 glioblastoma multiforme, and was rushed to Riley Hospital in Indianapolis for immediate surgery.

Before his diagnosis, Paul was a remarkable boy who charmed everyone he met with his dry sense of humor and playful approach to most things in life. Wicked smart, he could talk about nearly every professional and college football player as if he had been personally recruiting them. He not only knew their names and positions, he would cite some of their stats and recall plays from games as if he had it playing in slow motion in his head.

After surgery that removed the tumor and parts of his brain, Paul had difficulty hearing, or more accurately, processing spoken language. To this day, I can't imagine how scary it must be to wake up one day and not understand what others are saying. I was at the hospital when he awoke from the surgery and also visited him most days for several weeks afterward. During all those visits, I never heard Paul complain. He politely asked me and others to write things down so he could read what they were saying.

More than anyone I've ever met, Paul ended up teaching me the power of laughter. When I first started visiting Paul, my heart ached for him, and I didn't know what to say to him. In fact, I struggled not to cry when seeing this brilliant, energetic boy lying in a bed with nothing but noise from his surroundings filling his head. However, almost immediately, he would make self-deprecating jokes like, "Sorry, I'm like an old man. I have trouble hearing."

Later, Paul received radiation therapy (causing him to lose his hair) and took high doses of steroids (causing him to gain considerable weight). Those who hadn't seen him for a few months didn't recognize him. But when people would see him and give him that look of pity or concern, he would crack another "old man" joke—coaching others that it was okay to laugh, and perhaps more importantly, reminding us that despite his physical transformation, the same Pauly who we knew and loved was still inside.

Paul wasn't able to play the sports that he had loved previously and struggled playing card games and board games. But because of his attitude, instead of me sorrowfully sitting by Paul's side, I told silly stories. He had two little stuffed monkeys named Jailor and Brownie. Although he originally had them with him for snuggles and comfort, I couldn't let two monkeys not put on a show. Unlike Monkey and George, they rarely transformed into action heroes; they were comedians. Paul would crack up laughing at their performances. And the more he laughed, the more I laughed—not artificial, polite chuckles, but true belly-aching laughter. Some would mistakenly say that it was nice for me to make him laugh. They failed to understand that Paul was the one helping me.

Until one day when his laughter stopped. After fighting the disease for over a year, Paul's condition worsened. The medicine, the tumor, and his situation and prognosis clawed not just at his body, but attacked his playful personality. On February 12, 2013, Paul passed away with his mom and dad by his side.

Our entire family gathered a few days later for the memorial service. This time there wouldn't be any baseball or basketball games and nobody wanted to sing. None of Dad's inventions or investments and not even Monkey and George could bring back the lifeless boy in a coffin or restore normalcy to our family. A part of our soul had been taken with Paul. As much as Mom, Dad, Kristi, Mark, and I missed Paul's cackling, the pain reverberated knowing that Jay—our basketball teammate, our baseball catcher, the drummer in our band, the hand behind Monkey and George—had to endure the pain from the loss of his son.

As I walked to the coffin to see the little guy who had given all of us so much joy and taught me so much, I had to wonder, *How does one go on from something like this? How could Jay—how could we—pick up the pieces and pretend that we were whole again?* In the coffin, Paul's body rested peacefully, free from the monster that had been tormenting him. His little hands held Jailor and Brownie, the comedians who would also go to rest with Paul—but who would also serve as the final lesson that Paul would want us to know.

We go on because we must. We find a way to listen even when

we cannot hear. A family sticks together in good times and bad. We play together, work together, celebrate together, and mourn together because family is forever—even when members of it pass away. We remember and treasure those who have gone and support those who are still here. And, even though we may cry today, we live another day knowing that the world is made better because of each other's laughter.

CHAPTER 5:

SPECIAL

Life Lesson: Laugh until it hurts. And when it hurts, heal.

CANCER DIDN'T REMAIN CONTENT STAYING hidden in my stomach. It wanted more. My tests had my doctors puzzled. According to my PET/CT scans, my lymph nodes were enlarged and highly active, an indication the cancer had spread. However, my biopsy of some tissue from a few lymph nodes came back benign, suggesting perhaps the tumor was isolated to my stomach. If the cancer had not spread, the surgeon felt they should act quickly to remove my stomach—in hopes of getting the cancer out before it had a chance to spread. Although removing my stomach would be a major surgery, it was my best chance at survival.

The lesion that had appeared on my rectum had been removed as a precaution, almost incidentally, when they were adding the port in my chest for treatment and gathering biopsies of my lymph nodes. The surgeon and my oncologist were confident that it was nothing related.

That is, they were confident *until* the pathology reports returned. The pathology report classified the tissue cells as *poorly differentiated adenocarcinoma,* the same form of cancer that had been found in my stomach. If true, it was confirmation that the cancer had metastasized—classifying my cancer as stage 4 and taking the option of surgery off the table.

During my consultation visit to discuss the pathology report, the surgeon began by saying, "You are a special patient."

Humor had become my main coping mechanism. So, even though I knew he was referring to my complex situation, I still tried to ease the tension by quipping, "Thanks. I try to show up on time and do my part to make my visits pleasant for you."

The surgeon politely chuckled. "Well, you are a special patient for *two* reasons. We do think you are pleasant," he said, smiling, then continued, "but your situation also is puzzling. It is extraordinarily rare for your form of cancer to present itself as it has for you."

He explained that he and Dr. Helft had been discussing options. They questioned the pathology report. And if the pathology report was wrong, there would be no unwinding the clock later. They both agreed removing my stomach was what they would recommend—hoping that by acting quickly they could stop the spread of the cancer.

But before my surgery was even scheduled, another sore began showing up on my chin. It looked like a pimple, but had a hard base that appeared to be growing inward. At first I thought it was an ingrown hair, but since it wasn't going away, I asked Dr. Helft about it on my next visit. He had a dermatologist look at it, who also thought it looked more like an ingrown hair and not anything cancerous in nature or of concern. But to be certain, a cytologist stuck a needle in the sore and removed some tissue to examine under a microscope. She acknowledged that surprisingly it looked like cancerous tissue. The pathology report confirmed her assessment. It also was adenocarcinoma.

My cancer had definitely metastasized. It had not only spread, it was continuing to spread—even while I was on chemotherapy. So, removing my stomach no longer remained a viable option, not because it was too risky, but because it was already too late.

The sore on my chin continued to rapidly grow. I thought it was cancer's hateful way of making sure it stayed the center of attention. It wasn't enough to disrupt my personal life; it wanted to make sure others could see it. It must have resented that I was continuing to go to work each day and spending my evenings shuttling the girls to activities and helping them with their homework. Despite the chaos leaking into our home, I told Tonya that I wanted to cling to normalcy the best I could for as long as I could. But apparently, cancer felt neglected, so it placed itself squarely on the center of my chin, forcing others and myself to visibly see its ugliness. A week later, another lesion popped up on the back of my neck.

I tried to stay hopeful and focus on each day. Thanks to prayers, positive thoughts, and supportive friends, I could find peace in my situation. I would spend about fifteen minutes a day feeling sorry for myself, standing in the shower letting the water pour over my head, drowning in my own self-pity. But then I passed the rest of my days facing the day the best I could and taking time to be thankful for each new moment.

That's not to say I didn't have my emotional moments. My eyes would fill with tears at the smallest of things at times, like when the girls started the new school year. I wouldn't be there to squirt them with water on the last day of the school year, a tradition I had started when they were little. But I also continued to laugh. Life was not only precious to me, it was still silly and satirical. I laughed at memories and cackled at new frivolous moments, like forming a conga line with Bailor, Tonya's sister's dog who I had started calling my "spirit animal" because he seemed to understand me. The more that life was being pulled away from me, the more I tried to savor in the life I had remaining. And, I told myself that cancer could take my life, but until that final moment, it couldn't take my laugh or smile.

For the next three weeks, the angry sore on my chin continued to grow until I went in for a special type of surgery, a Mohs surgery, to have it and the sore on the back of my neck removed. I was introduced to the talented surgeon, Dr. Ally-Khan Somani, whose exuberant personality made me feel immediately at ease. After a nurse took some pictures of my sore, he made some markings on my face and explained the game plan. "It's like removing a tree," he said with jovial confidence. "I can take measurements of how tall the tree is above the surface, but until I start digging, we don't really know how deep the roots may go," adding how he would "keep digging until all the roots were removed, but also be careful to not dig any deeper than necessary." He described how he would excise one layer of tissue below the surface, look at it under a microscope and determine if we got all the cancerous tissue out or not. If we did, we're done. If not, we repeat the process.

After a few numbing shots into my chin, the excavating began. Apparently, my tree had deep roots. It took three rounds of digging. In between each round, Dr. Somani examined the tissues in a microscope and checked on me to see how I was doing. During one of his visits, he casually mentioned how the cells were "poorly differentiated"—the same words that prefaced my original diagnosis: *poorly differentiated adenocarcinoma.*

I asked him what the words meant exactly.

Since IU Health University Hospital is both a referral hospital and an academic teaching hospital, Dr. Somani is also a professor of clinical dermatology. My question made his eyes glisten as if I was one of his curious students eager to learn.

"Great question!" He gushed, "Imagine you have a gang who all dress similar: white T-shirt, blue jeans, leather coat, and one gold earring. Someone dressed identical is likely to be a member of that gang, right? Likewise, you might be able to accurately conclude someone wearing a red cap, black sweats, and white high top shoes as being part of another gang. This is how it works with normal healthy cells. Although there may be thousands of cells, they are recognizable and can be easily classified by the way they look."

Dr. Somani paused for emphasis and continued, "But now, suppose you start to see changes in how a few of the gang members are dressed. Someone who has a white T-shirt, blue jeans, leather coat, and one *silver* earring may still be associated as being a member of the first gang. This is how unhealthy cancerous cells begin. They look like variations of a healthy cell and are more easily classified. However, as time elapses and more variations occur, you may end up with an entirely different look—think of someone wearing black pants, plaid shirt, stocking hat... You name it!" he added, raising his voice for a moment. "My point is that they become hard to recognize and hard to classify into the appropriate group. Similarly, as cancer cells spread and grow, they become less recognizable. It becomes hard to tell what they are exactly. In other words, they become *poorly differentiated*."

Not only did his explanation help me understand the term; it gave me insight into my situation. The cancer cells on my chin and in my body were growing, spreading, and adapting. The tumor had not only grown outward on my chin; it had indeed grown inward. And it was growing aggressively, burrowing its way through my body like a hungry groundhog.

Feeling confident he had removed the remaining cancer cells on his third excision, Dr. Somani handed me a mirror like a hairstylist showing off their cut. He cheerfully described his methodology, but the lesson he wanted to teach me was lost on me. I could only focus on the gaping hole in my face and wondered whether or not he could put me back together again. With a needle and thread and an extra pair of hands from a nurse, he swiftly stitched me up as if I was a teddy bear with a small tear at the seam.

At first, Dr. Somani wasn't too concerned with the lesion on the back of my neck. He didn't think it was related and was likely benign, but he agreed to remove it as a precaution. As he sliced into the tissue, his playful chatty demeanor transformed into extended quiet focus, speaking only when instructing others in the room to hand him additional instruments. After he finished with his work, he explained that it indeed looked cancerous and appeared to be growing directly into the tissue surrounding the tumor making it appear "metastatic in nature." Later the pathology report would classify the tissue from my neck and my chin as poorly differentiated adenocarcinoma, the same type of cancer found in my stomach.

I was impressed with the speed, precision, and tidiness of Dr. Somani's work. Nonetheless, slicing through the tender tissues in my chin made even small facial movements painful. Even a smile would cause me to ache. I felt dejected and defeated, like I was fighting an unwinnable battle. The stitches in my ass had been uncomfortable and annoying, but the stitches in my face didn't just restrict my movement, it stole my personality. Cancer had literally taken away my ability to smile.

As Tonya drove me home, I gazed at the trees out the window thinking about the depth of their roots hidden beneath the soil. What had they endured to reach their heights and how much longer would they stand? I almost asked Tonya to slow down—hating that each tree came in and out of view so quickly, appearing and vanishing in a matter of seconds. My eyes focused on a barren tree with only a few leaves clinging to its branches. The decaying tree was standing, but was that still considered living?

Already cancer made its presence known by becoming a punch to my gut, kick in my ass, pain in my neck, and punch to my face. It would not stop until it was given the full attention and recognition it deserved. It wasn't enough to be the cause for my pain. It needed others to witness my suffering and deterioration.

I felt foolish for being hopeful. I felt like a fraud pretending I could beat this. I allowed myself to feel the pain, not only in my face and in my gut, but the emotional pain I had been so determined to push away.

I wasn't special. I was just another patient in the grips of terminal cancer.

CHAPTER 6:

TETHERBALL

Life Lesson: Don't get roped into negativity. Hang on to positivity.

WHEN I WAS A STUDENT at Ferdinand Elementary School in Ferdinand, Indiana, there was a lower elementary for grades K–3 and an upper elementary building that served grades 4–6. The two schools shared a library located in the upper elementary building. As a third grader, my classmates and I had to walk outside to get to the library. It was a short walk, but a dangerous one, or at least it was dangerous for me on one fateful day. (Cue ominous music.) The weapon that got me was a tetherball.

Since tetherballs have largely disappeared from playgrounds (perhaps because of stories like this one), allow me to explain the fundamentals of the game. The construction of a tetherball consists of sticking a pole vertically in the ground (or concrete-filled tire) with a rope fastened to the top of the pole and attaching a ball on the other end of the rope that hangs and swings about waist-height. The objective of the game is to serve the ball in one direction and to keep smacking it until the rope wraps completely around the pole. Meanwhile, on the other side of the pole, your opponent tries to knock the ball in the opposite direction, also trying to wrap the rope around the pole. The first player to successfully wrap the rope in their direction wins. Tetherball was a fun game and had become a staple on most playgrounds. Ferdinand Elementary had one in the parking lot in front of the school, which doubled as our playground and tragically became part of the crime scene that perilous morning.

My classmates and I were on our short voyage to the upper elementary and happened to walk past the iconic tetherball in our path. In one moment I was discussing the latest episode of *The Dukes of Hazzard*, and the next moment I was lassoed around the neck with a tetherball robe. Apparently, another friend—out of playfulness and natural childish exuberance—pounded the ball without realizing I was within its grasp...or maybe he was tired of hearing me question whether Bo and Luke Duke did their own stunts. At any rate, in one moment I was bee-boppin' along, telling my stories...and then in the next, I was dangling from a tetherball pole like a piñata with the rope coiled around my neck, my storytelling having come to an abrupt end.

Fortunately, my classmates didn't use this as an opportunity to beat me with sticks and see if candy came out of me. Someone untangled me before the strangling could finish me. And, although it was scary, I was fine. My mom left her work to pick me up from school and dropped me off at Aunt Mary's house to spend the day watching cartoons and drinking milkshakes. So, overall, it wasn't a bad day. But it did leave a pretty bad rope burn around my neck, which certainly caused most strangers to look twice when seeing me.

I still like tetherballs. And, no, I didn't file a complaint or lawsuit with Tetherball Incorporated, but the fact that the game seemed to rapidly start disappearing from playgrounds in the years to come made me wonder if other schools suffered a similar series of events. The whole experience also taught me as a young kid that something that appeared so harmless and fun could possibly be dangerous.

I think of people who regularly complain about other people or circumstances as tetherballs. Their behavior often seems like a fun, playful force that wants to drag you into an innocent game of smacking something around. It's the person who complains about it being a Monday. The person on a soccer field who thinks their kid would be a champion if the coach was doing their job. It's the person always complaining about being too hot or too cold. It's the colleague who disagrees with every idea, but never proposes a different solution. It's the friend who asks about your day, but then interrupts to talk about how horrible their day was. It's the worker who points out the problems of every procedure that they have to follow at work, but then really gets mad if a change is made. It's the person who always has a friend problem or relationship problem. It's the pot stirrer who says things like, "Joey, did you see what Bobby had on today?" But also goes to Bobby and says, "Don't you think Joey is too opinionated about what people wear?"

It's also the people who indulge in "parking lot conversations."

During a two-hour meeting designed to hash out a plan for a project, these people sit quietly exchanging painful looks at each other and then rush into the parking lot to let out their true feelings. In the parking lot, they talk about how they disagree with the plan and how it's going to fail. And, then, they start taking jabs at the ball, tightening the force around everyone who spoke in favor of the plan. They didn't have the courage to disagree in the meeting, but instead find pleasure in whacking the ball at them instead.

My advice: Don't become entangled in the spiteful and toxic game of attacking others or complaining about situations. Don't let the rope begin to drag you in, because the result is suffocating. If you are the person taking whacks at the ball out of anger, there's a chance someone is in your path and you may not even realize it. If you are in the game watching someone else become entangled, help them get out of the noose. Playing the game feels so innocent, but the damage hurts everyone—not just to the person being hanged by the rope. It's more than an energy drain; it erodes trust in the entire team and builds a culture of complaining and back-stabbing.

I like to laugh and enjoy making others laugh. Sometimes that alone is the goal—to lighten the mood in order to bring joy to someone's day. Laughing *with* someone draws people together, boosts others' moods, reduces stress, and diminishes pain. But laughing *at* someone—making fun of others or targeting people who don't find the attack funny—is not at all the same. That doesn't lighten the mood; it adds stress and brings more weight and misery to everyone.

I don't think all conversations in work and life need to feel pleasant or funny. I simply want them to be constructive. Disagreements both in the workplace and with friends and family aren't just helpful, they are essential. I think any team or group dynamic is better when the intention is problem-solving. For example, if I stand in a parking lot and complain about the performance of a coworker, my behavior is toxic and strangling. However, if I genuinely talk with another colleague I trust and ask for advice on how to help a colleague improve their performance or constructively handle the situation, I'm unraveling the rope. At home, if I am complaining about how there is nothing to eat for dinner, all my ranting leaves me hungry and everyone else feeling injured. But if I take time to start cooking and maybe even convince my kids to help, everyone feels a little better, perhaps even empowered.

I fail at this myself frequently. But I also know the people I respect the most are positive people who problem-solve challenges. I admire the pilots landing a plane while trying to put out a fire in the cockpit, not the passengers who complain about being too warm. They are the people who don't pretend that their grass is greener, but seem to find beauty in their grass regardless of its color. They are the people who make me laugh, the people who make me think, and the people who make me better. I try to spend my time around these people and walk as quickly as possible past others who take jabs at the tetherball. If I have to engage in conversations with others wanting to play the game of tetherball, I find catching the ball and not hitting back is the quickest way to end the game.

One of my mentors early in my career was Denny Leathers, a guy who served as the business manager (school term for a Chief Financial Officer) for Danville Community Schools. Although Denny was a man who made a career of thoughtful decisions, apparently in one of his rare weak moments, he hired me as director of technology when I was only twenty-eight years old, and put me in charge of people nearly twice my age. I read books on leadership and even attended different conferences trying to become a better boss, but I was clueless. Fortunately, day after day, I watched Denny show up before anyone else arrived in the office and start the coffee. I listened to him make fun of himself even though the guy is brilliant. I heard him constantly ask questions to try to understand someone's point of view. The more inflamed a situation became, the calmer he responded. His goal was never to cast blame, but to find solutions. I saw him have the tough conversation of letting people go, but doing it with such honesty, dignity, and compassion that the person ended up thanking him at the end. Although I made fun of his nonstop whistling in the office, I found the silence on the days he wasn't there to be grating.

Denny and my work relationship was focused, productive, and professional, with a healthy dash of playfulness. He called me Cobra. I called him Mongoose. We pretended to cross paths in the hallway like two cowboys about to duel. We probably did disagree at times, but I don't remember one example in the fifteen years we worked together that felt like an argument. Our conversations focused on finding better answers to problems, not about fighting for who was right. And he loved his job. He loved people. He loved—and continues to love—life. And so still today, even though he's been retired for years, I want to spend as much time with him as possible, because I'm still learning from him and every time I see him, I feel a little smarter and a lot better.

Denny was one of the first guys to reach out to help me after my diagnosis. He knew exactly what to say that made me feel better, which really was three simple, yet powerful statements: "I'm so sorry you have to go through this. If anyone can beat this, I know it's you. How can I help?"

With those three statements, Denny spoke volumes. He told me that he cared, that he believed in me, and that he would be there to help. He became my driver and companion for many of my treatments. Often he would simply sit next to me during the treatments reading a book while I worked on my laptop. When we did talk, we would chat about things like politics, IU basketball, and my daughters and his grandkids. But he also wasn't afraid to ask about my health situation. He would ask questions that would help me process my options. He would offer suggestions. But mostly, he would just listen.

In the face of my diagnosis with cancer and evidence of it metasta-sizing, it would have been easy to blame others—the doctors, my genes, food manufacturers, the insurance company, Democrats, Republicans, others who don't seem to understand, those who don't believe in God, believers, God Himself—surely one of them was the villain.

But finding someone to blame wasn't going to give me a cure. And feeling bitter, angry, or defeated not only was counterproductive to my own health, it further tormented those I loved the most—who also carried the weight of the disease. Yes, I did reserve some time each day to feel sorry for myself and my family. I cried. I got angry. But ulti-mately, I realized that my next step had to be forward.

So, I tried to mimic my mentor, Denny, and stay calm, laugh at myself, and problem-solve. Like him, I tried to ask better questions of my doctors and others to understand my best options. Like him,

I tried to have honest conversations with people and let them know how I really felt. Like him, I tried to maintain a bounce in my step and a joyful whistle. And even on my bad days when I felt like I was at the end of my rope, people like Denny kept me tethered to hope.

CHAPTER 7:

THE PRICE
OF LIVING

*Life Lesson: Life is priceless, but you still
have to pay the medical bills.*

FORTUNATELY, THE TISSUES IN MY chin healed and smiling became
possible again. Getting back my grin and laugh didn't just boost my
mood, it fueled my will to fight through the next set of challenges
that would come my way. And although there is some merit to the
expression "laughter is the best medicine," I didn't think my goofy
laugh alone could fend off the cancer growing inside me. Fortunately,
I also received some encouraging news: My cancer was in fact associated with Lynch syndrome, which meant that it was at least medically
eligible for immunotherapy treatment. There was one problem: My
insurance denied coverage for the treatment.

My family and friends were extremely supportive. Even without
knowing the insurance situation, many had previously offered to help
in any way possible, including financially; I just needed to let them
know. They were a kind, generous group, but I had a difficult time

convincing myself—much less others—that this was an investment worth making. Each treatment costs around $25,000, and I would need to receive the treatment every three weeks for probably two years. Without even doing the math, I knew we didn't have that kind of money and some simple fundraiser wouldn't cover the shortage.

Furthermore, even if I could scrape together money for a few rounds of treatments, the more I analyzed the situation, the more I came to the same conclusion: I was a lousy investment. There were no guarantees and tons of associated risks. Although there were some remarkable isolated stories of incredible responses for some patients, those were the exceptions and not something one could expect. Early research suggested that only about ten percent of all metastatic gastric cancer patients on immunotherapy continued to live for two or more years. Furthermore, there was about the same percentage chance that the treatment itself would kill me.

I imagined myself pitching my case to a group of ten investors as if it were a business proposition. "Do I have a deal for you! All I need is a small down payment of a million dollars! What do you get in return, you ask? Oh, there's really no plan to give you back your money at the moment. Who will this help? Well, imagine all ten of you had metastatic gastric cancer. It might help one of you live for a couple more years. But, I also should inform you that it may cause one of you taking the treatment to die. Okay, who is ready to sign up?"

It made no sense to me. I wanted to live. I wanted to be there for my girls and hated the thought of leaving them. But I also couldn't imagine taking money I had worked all my adult life to save for our retirement and for the girls' colleges and placing it on a bet that was considered a long shot. Not only would I be gone, but I would leave my family with nothing, except a financial burden. And if I wasn't willing to invest in the idea, how could I possibly ask others? I wasn't being a defeatist. I wasn't being humble. I wasn't being proud. I was simply being real and honest. And the truth became rather straightforward to me: I wasn't worth it.

And yet, it was clearly my best shot. Unlike chemo, which attacks all rapidly-dividing cells within the body, immunotherapy works by triggering the body's natural immune system to recognize and attack specific cancer cells. Chemotherapy reminded me of the chemicals my dad would use to treat algae in our pond when I was a kid. I would row a little jon boat around the pond watching Dad reach into a container that included scary statements like *Danger: Hazards to Humans and Domestic Animals*, tossing the blue pellets into the water. Sometimes it did help kill the algae. Sometimes it just slowed its growth. And, sometimes, it did very little to kill the algae but instead killed some of our fish.

Immunotherapy, on the other hand, reminded me of the grass carp Dad added to the pond one year. The herbivore fish were introduced into the pond with the hope that they would naturally seek out, eat, and eliminate the algae and grass problems. Although I was skeptical when my dad explained how these freaky-looking fish eat slime, I couldn't deny the results. It really did work!

There were some big differences from our pond slime remedy and my cancer treatment options. For one thing, clear evidence showed that chemotherapy would at best slow the growth of the slime (tumors) in my body; it would not destroy it. The slowed growth of cancer cells would be temporary in nature, and the scum would undoubtedly rapidly grow shortly after the treatments stopped. And, unfortunately, although immunotherapy was intended to transform my own immune system into a cancer-eating carp, it wasn't as innocuous as the little herbivores devouring seaweed in our pond. Things could go badly. My own cancer-eating carp might ignore the slime and instead start attacking other fish and organisms (healthy organs in my body). There was certainly no guarantee and lots of risk, but immunotherapy brought the *possibility* of survival. It brought hope.

There were only two groups I was willing to ask for financial help: my health insurance and the pharmaceutical companies. I rationalized that they were in the business of investing some money in the short term for one patient if the results could generate a lot of money in the long term from several patients. Dr. Helft had tried a couple of times to get approval from my insurance company, but the request had come back denied. For my form of cancer, immunotherapy was considered second-line therapy, meaning it could only be used if more common forms of treatment, like chemotherapy, were tried and proven not to be working.

Tonya and Dr. Helft filed a separate appeal and continued to make a case on my behalf. After all, despite the uncertainty of immunotherapy, it was statistically proven to be more effective than chemotherapy in my situation. They both also reached out to a couple of the drug manufacturers for financial assistance. However, since the drugs had been recently FDA approved and I had already started chemotherapy, I wasn't eligible for any of the trials. The only option—really my last chance—was in the hands of my insurance.

I felt like I had been ejected from a plane and was spiraling help-lessly to the ground. Even though my main chute (chemotherapy) clearly had holes in its design, it was hard to hope for its failure just so I could try out the reserve chute (immunotherapy). With each moment that passed, I was plummeting downward with the risk of waiting too long.

Each day I would go through the mail as if a golden ticket was tucked away in each envelope. But with each new letter opened, I became less hopeful that I was going to hit the jackpot. I also became more keenly aware of the expenses already accumulating from my past surgeries, doctor visits, and rounds of chemotherapy. People were tell-ing me to stay strong and be brave, but with stitches in my face and a cancer that seemed determined to grow, I began to ask myself, "When is saying 'Stop, that's enough' actually the bravest thing to do?"

And then, with little fanfare one evening, I opened a letter that stated, *Based on the information provided to us, we are pleased to autho-rize benefits for service(s) referenced above.* I scanned the table assuming it was perhaps for an upcoming PET/CT scan but instead my eyes caught the word *Pembrolizumab*, commonly branded Keytruda, a form of immunotherapy made by Merck. I read the letter over and over, making sure I wasn't mistaken and almost fearful that the text would change if I looked away. Immunotherapy seemed to be covered. This could be my chance at survival.

Ironically, the next day I received another letter from my insur-ance company. Once again, a table at the top listed *Pembrolizumab.* However, this time, the text below the table read, *Based on the review of the information provided to us, the service referenced above is not medically necessary, as that term is defined under your health benefit plan. Services which are not medically necessary are a benefit exclusion and therefore not a covered benefit.* My heart dropped to my stomach. I looked at the date of the letter and ran to look at the letter I had received only the day before. The letter denying coverage was one day newer than the letter approving coverage.

So, I had two letters: one that opened the door to a treatment that could save my life and another one that categorically shut the door to the same treatment. I didn't know what to do. I didn't want to pretend to ignore the new letter and begin treatment—that approach could go badly for my family, with us being stuck with the entire cost. I could call the insurance company for clarification, but I was scared: It was literally a matter of life and death. The right thing to do was to know the truth, even if I didn't want to hear it.

Tonya volunteered to call the insurance company. Fortunately, she was assured that my insurance would in fact cover the treatment! We never did learn why we received the other letter that rejected coverage and never learned why the decision had changed from previous letters. But we also didn't care. Immunotherapy gave me a chance.

Fully knowing the risks involved, now we had to wonder, would the medicine we had fought so hard for me to take also be the very concoction that would cause my immune system to attack my healthy organs? Would this be my cancer-fighting miracle medicine or would this be the potion that poisoned me?

I lay awake at night imagining a mob of thugs chasing me—only to find myself at the edge of a cliff overlooking a river with nowhere else to run or hide. I had been hoping for a cliff—something, anything that might help me escape. But looking over the edge, I realized now that my escape route was anything but ordinary and was itself inherently dangerous. But still, I knew that standing still was even more dangerous. So, with little time to think deeply about the fall, I turned and jumped.

CHAPTER 8:

LUCKY

Life Lesson: Sometimes it's better to be lucky than good. But most of the time, it's better to be good.

DESIGN AND CONSTRUCT A SOLUTION *that will allow a light bulb to be safely dropped from four floors above the ground.*

That was my first assignment as a freshman at Ball State University in the architecture design studio class. In addition to building a solution that would prevent the light bulb from getting damaged in the drop, we were asked to create a design symbolic of ourselves and that made the launch and flight interesting to spectators. And, there would be spectators. The launch would happen from within the architecture building's open atrium while the students and staff of the entire five-year-program watched. The project would not be graded, but clearly it would be evaluated. This was the rite of passage for all the new architecture students.

Nearly all of my new classmates were cut from the same mold—they were all overachievers. Determined. Creative. Perfectionists. We had four days to build our solution. As students of one of the top three architecture programs in the country, we knew that being accepted into the program also came with sacrifice. All-nighters were just part of what it took to create something special. So, we all worked—literally day and night—in perfecting our solutions.

We each approached the task in our own way. I went with what I knew: a basic rocket-type design, with a deployable parachute. I tediously drew crumbling bricks on my shuttle, symbolizing my confidence of being more than three hours away from home at college in Muncie, Indiana and the crack of uncertainty I felt in this new chapter of my life. The design represented my launch into adulthood, as if to say I was simultaneously ready and scared for the adventure.

My launching mechanism was goofy and lame, nothing more than a board that would mount on the railing. The board balanced on the edge like a seesaw; on one end sat my rocket, ready to drop, and on the other end its counterweight, a mechanical little toy monster that walked when it heard noise.

My plan was simple: I would get the crowd to clap and cheer, spurring my monster to walk toward the rocket, shifting the balance to cause the rocket and the monster to fall. The monster would be tied off to keep him from dropping. The rocket would drop, with a simple ripcord that deployed the parachute, allowing the rocket and light bulb a safe descent.

The design itself didn't take too long to build, but I only got a few hours of sleep the entire four days because I was spending so much time trying to make my bricks look authentic. I was proud of my work until I started to see other students' designs. Others didn't build a silly-looking rocket with a parachute. Their models looked like something out of a sci-fi movie. One design had the light bulb tucked inside a giant transparent cube with neon lights taped along each edge. The light bulb was suspended in the center of the cube, making it look like a crown jewel inside a translucent display case at a museum.

All the students worked tirelessly on their designs, spending days and nights in the studio. That is everyone except Luke who didn't work on his project at all. For four days and nights his studio desk sat empty. He would come in each night to talk with us, but he literally didn't work on his project for a minute. When we asked him his plan, he casually retorted that he would figure something out. As each hour and day passed, we all started to squirm with unease thinking of being in Luke's shoes. What would he do when the final moment came for him to launch his solution in the crowd of spectators—with all the students and professors staring?! But Luke didn't seem to worry.

The launch day finally came. All of us were gathered in the studio room making final touches and inspections on our capsules that would be carrying their precious cargo, a simple light bulb, with eager spectators looking on. About an hour before the launch, Luke came into the studio, still with absolutely nothing done. By this point, we all assumed he would not participate. But Luke started to walk around the studio grabbing scraps of newspaper, cardboard, plastic, and waste from other projects scattered on the floor. He shoved the loose items together in a ball, with duct tape somehow holding things together. He stuck the light bulb in the center of the amoeba and used more tape to hold the bulb in place. His "design" literally looked like a pile of trash.

When we carried our contraptions to the location of the launch, I was nervous for my own launch, but also nervous for the reaction that Luke was about to receive. One by one, we stood on the ledge with the students and staff cheering us on. The loudness of cheers corresponded with how impressed the crowd was with each student's solution to the challenge. My rocket dropped from the edge after the movement of my mechanical monster. It did what it was supposed to do. It dropped safely, slowly, predictably. The crowd gave my four-day project a courteous applause. From where everyone was standing, not a single person would have been able to see any of the artwork I had labored over. In the end, it was just a rocket with a parachute floating to the ground. The student who built the neon cube got some loud cheers, not just because of its translucent center, but because it bounced after striking the ground and held the light bulb safely inside.

Then Luke's turn came. He had found some giant elastic strap in the studio, which he duct-taped to the ledge. He walked up to the ledge with his ball of trash. I could barely watch as the crowd looked on with bewilderment as he squeezed his rubble inside the elastic strap. But giving him the benefit of the doubt, the crowd gave him the cue for his launch like they had for others before him, chanting, "Three! Two! One! Blast off!"

Luke pulled back on the elastic strap like he was about to launch a water balloon through the glass windows across from our launch position. With his trash wedged inside, he stretched it as far as he could and then released it.

His wad of paper arched through the air like a rock flying from a slingshot. The crowd roared! The object contracted, and began plummeting to the ground like a pelican diving for a fish. It fell one flight, then the old newspapers and trash bags spread outward, giving new shape and new flight to the object in motion. The ball of garbage pulled out of its downward spiral and seemed to transform into a hummingbird—pausing in its descent mid-flight. For a moment, the creature seemed to stare back at its audience, making sure all had taken notice, then tucked in its head and wings, transforming back into its dive position and continued downward. I found myself screaming "Whoa!" with the crowd watching this amazing maneuver in flight. When it was only ten feet from smashing into the ground, it puffed out like a jellyfish, and floated gracefully to the floor.

The building erupted with cheers and thunderous applause. It was spectacular—by far the best launch that would happen the entire day, perhaps in the entire history of this long tradition. Luke's design was legendary!

Luke had no idea that his last-minute concoction would pull off these stunts. In fact, we tried to replicate the spectacle later, but neither Luke nor anyone else could repeat the amazing flight we all witnessed. Luke hadn't meticulously planned for a launch that would clearly be the crowd's favorite—he had made up the whole thing at the last minute. Luke simply got lucky.

I learned a couple of valuable life lessons that day: We all get lucky sometimes, and even a ball of trash can be beautiful.

. . .

Cancer had become my ball of trash. Now, I needed Luke's luck.

A predator resided inside my gut. I imagined it steadily chewing through me, little by little, wanting to leave my suffering in full display for those who loved me most. The images of seeing past cancer patients' bodies deteriorate, people I knew and loved, haunted me. I hated the thought of going through it myself and dreaded the idea of my girls seeing me that way.

None of this felt fair—not just to me, but to my family. My girls deserved better. They should not have to go through something like this at a time in their lives when they should be stressing over what the correct answer is on their math quiz, or deciding what jeans to wear to school, or hoping they get a good seating assignment on the bus.

In my moments of sorrow and self-pity, I wanted to scream, "How could we be so unlucky?"

But then I looked at all the blessings I had already been given, that my entire family had been given, and I realized we were still among the lucky ones. Through no action or choices of my own, I was born into a loving family, with nurturing parents and supportive siblings. I grew up in a nice town with a great school with caring teachers and was surrounded by amazing people. I got a good education, went to college, met fabulous friends, and landed my first job as a math teacher in Monticello, Indiana.

I was lucky that Tonya taught in the classroom adjacent to mine, and that she liked to read the *New York Times* each Sunday, so she drove to West Lafayette—where I lived at the time—to buy her paper. I was lucky she was willing to join me for breakfast during those trips, where we got to know each other. I was lucky our friendship continued to grow until we became more than friends. I married my best friend, and I was lucky she was an amazing mother. I was lucky both our kids were born healthy and continued to grow with curiosity and kindness and ultimately taught me more than I could ever teach them. And, through it all, different jobs and life situations surrounded me with caring people who were there to laugh with me and cry with me. I was lucky to have so many people thinking and praying for my family and me. And because of that strength from others, I tried to focus on what I had been given, rather than what I was about to lose.

I also thought about how the events had unfolded, giving me a chance of survival. Tonya's sister, Jenny, worked for Dr. Rex, a world-renowned gastroenterologist at IU Health University Hospital. Dr. Rex not only provided my diagnosis, but referred me to Dr. Paul Helft, my oncologist, who also is among the best. And, my luck wasn't just built on knowing my wife, whose sister knew the right doctor, who connected me with another doctor, who was willing to plead my case with my insurance company—it was built on all the patients that came before me who were willing to use immunotherapy as an experimental drug. My luck existed because there were doctors, scientists, and research specialists who refused to accept that chemo and radiation alone were sufficient. Despite being told it was impossible, they continued to believe it's possible to treat cancer by triggering our own immune system to attack it. I was lucky my diagnosis happened when it did, rather than three years earlier.

Although I was apprehensive about starting immunotherapy, I felt lucky to be on it. There were three possibilities: 1) it wouldn't work, and I would die from the cancer; 2) it would cause my immune system to mistakenly attack other healthy cells in my body, and I would die from the treatment; or 3) it would work, and save or at least extend my life. Certainly, I hoped for the third option, but I took comfort in knowing that regardless of what happened, I was already lucky for the life I had and the treatment I was given.

I also felt peace in knowing that if option one or two came true, the doctors would learn from my situation, which could possibly help other patients. Even though I hated having my family face the garbage that came with the disease, I was hopeful that they too would somehow find a way to learn from it, grow from it, and emerge from it.

Perhaps my situation, my ball of trash, could also turn into something beautiful.

CHAPTER 9:

THE ORDINARY THINGS

Life Lesson: Turn doing dishes into your wishes.

My FIRST ROUND OF IMMUNOTHERAPY was uneventful. It didn't kill me, and I didn't have any terrible side effects. After my treatment I felt…well, pretty normal. And suddenly feeling normal felt fantastic. Normalcy—it was precisely what I craved the most.

As I savored the ordinary day-to-day routines of working, shuttling my kids to practices, and doing dishes and other household chores, I thought about Tonya and my trip to Bali in 2013 and how everyone we encountered seemed so content and present in the moment. Tonya had wanted to visit Bali for some time because of its reputation for natural beauty. So when we learned that our friend, Mindy, had signed up to teach English at a school for students with disabilities that summer, we immediately made plans for our visit.

After going through the hectic immigration and customs line at the airport, we jumped in a taxi to travel to the room we had reserved.

Staring out the window of the taxi's back seat, I was struck by the seemingly chaotic and disorderly appearance of our surroundings. The lanes on the road seemed to serve as only a suggestion to each driver. Cars and motorbikes would squeeze any place they could fit to keep advancing forward—weaving in and out of traffic, honking their horns with each pass. The busy streets were filled with food-cart vendors, market goers, and sellers who carried baskets of food and supplies on their heads. Chickens walked freely along the streets, in the yards of most of the modest homes, and casually strolled into local restaurants and markets as if they were customers perusing the day's deals. As we zoomed down the narrow, poorly paved roads in that first taxi trip, barely dodging other vehicles, pedestrians, and chickens, I began to question the sanity of us picking this as a relaxing getaway for two weeks.

But then, as the days passed and our adventures continued, I fell in love with the island and its people. I marveled at the endless rice terraces of Ubud, the cool breezes and lush mountains and valleys enclosing Munduk, the lakes and natural hot springs flanked by craters and active volcanoes of the central mountains, the white sand stretching out to the turquoise waters of the Blue Lagoon in Padangbai, the ubiquitous Bob Marley tunes playing in the background on Gili Trawangan, the pure coral beaches surrounding Gili Meno, the marvelous skies with trippy clouds, brilliant stars and serene sunsets of Lembongan, and the surfers disappearing into the night off the towering cliffs of Bingin.

But even more than those memories, I fell in love with the kind and beautiful people we met who helped guide us in our journey and those who added a helping hand or added to our experiences. Gede was our driver who led us to and from Munduk. In addition to his warm demeanor, we occasionally would witness his playful sense of humor, like when he informed us of how Bali's most expensive coffee, Kopi Luwak, is harvested from the feces of a luwak. Kutut, our guide to the top of Mount Batur, held unwavering confidence and patience for us as we slowly made our way up. Darta, our dive master at Padangbai, assisted us with a constant warm smile, joyful eyes, and a helpful spirit I found to be reassuring and comforting when breathing air from a tank underwater. Jay, the no-nonsense, organized, best-dressed (snappy underwater attire) dive master patience was the perfect balance to Eurie, the carefree, self-titled Scandinavian "water clown" who bubbled with enthusiasm when describing the beauty of local marine life. We also received a hearty "hello" and helpful hand from countless strangers with whom we crossed paths, who regularly had to point us in the right direction.

We also had wonderful shared experiences with people who came from all over the world to see this beautiful country. We compared travel itineraries with a couple from Japan in a spa in Ubud, relaxed in the hot springs of Munduk with a group of Australians, discussed the best places to travel with some Americans on our hike to a waterfall, fell off the beaten path with a mother and daughter from Switzerland, made light of our boating and transport experiences with a young French couple, dove with some honeymooners from the UK, and watched a Scandinavian learn French in a dive company managed by a German. We also had the delight of having our friend Mindy along with us through much of the trip serving at times as our guide, photographer, and co-adventurer. Everywhere we went we witnessed the melting pot of languages and culture.

Certainly, there were some traditions of Bali that disturbed me, like seeing women carrying enormous loads on their heads, with men directing them as if the women were mere pack goats. The temples posted signs forbidding women to enter during their menstrual period because they consider bleeding women dangerous and impure. In addition to some of these unjust practices, the small, rugged huts in the rice fields were not the kind of a home I would want for my girls.

It's also easy to look at a place like Bali and find fascination in all that is different. Food, religions, rituals, dress, vegetation, climate, their calendar and language are all so different. And, yet, in looking through my photos and reflecting on the trip, I can't help but notice all that we have in common. Little kids playing in tide pools reminded me of my girls swimming in a nearby aquatic center when they were toddlers. Two boys having stick fights mimicked my nephew, Charlie, with his Star Wars saber. And as I watched a young lady and man playfully laughing at each other, I couldn't help but think of Tonya and me taking classes together at Purdue when we started dating.

Those who helped us often added the phrase "slowly, slowly" to their instructions. Gede said it before we opened the back door of the taxi on a busy street. Kutut said it as he coached us through our steps up the mountain. The guide that we encountered on our trip to the waterfall said it as we came upon the narrow paths. Darta said it right before we started to descend below the waves in the Badung Strait. The words are spoken as if they hold greater meaning than to simply slow your pace—and they seem to guide not just the movement of your body, but also your state of mind. The people of Bali seem proud of what they have, rather than disappointed in what they don't have. They are strong and determined, yet seem to avoid the rat race mentality of hurrying through life. They seem content in the moment. They are thankful for their blessings.

Slowly, slowly. The motto has less to do with time management or reducing the number of hours worked in a day. The Balinese seem to work long hours every day of the week. But their grateful, reflective spirit allows them to enjoy, almost savor, the moment they are in—truly living in the moment and giving thanks for the ordinary things.

Throughout my life, I've had a long list of reasons to be thankful, namely my family, my friends, my job, and my health. But after my diagnosis with cancer, much like the people of Bali, I started to see the world through a different perspective. Despite all the terrible things that came with this disease, it also allowed me to see things more clearly—as if viewing them through a magnifying glass—drawing focus on the small details that give me peace, strength, hope, and joy. In the past, although I would have called my family, friends, job, and my health blessings, I also would have complained or groaned at the challenges or trivial obstacles that come with each. But after my diagnosis, it was the small moments that propelled me forward: my first breath each morning, drinking a cup of coffee without it cramping my stomach, the crunching sound of my kids eating (as I remind them to chew with their mouths closed), a pigeon peeking out of a gutter and into my office (the same pigeon that I used to cuss at for pooping on our porch), the strength to shower and dress, an uneventful and painless bowel movement (since my medicine didn't always play nicely with my regularity), having a decent night of sleep without pain or discomfort. These were all things that suddenly made me happy.

My trip to Bali reminded me that we are all one species living on this planet. We all love. We all suffer. We all die. But also, we are all given a chance to live. We have a choice on whether to focus on the struggles we face or the blessings we've been given. My cancer diagnosis taught me that peace doesn't just come from good days. It comes from moments we choose to see as good. Helping my kids with homework, unloading the dishwasher, sweeping the floor, and completing daily routines were no longer chores chewing *into* my time. They were reminders to appreciate that I've been *given* this time. They served as affirmations that I was still strong. I was still standing. I was still here.

When in the thick of life's obstacles, it's easy to see our experiences at times as overwhelming, noisy, messy—perhaps similar to my first impression of Bali. But all of the noise and all of the messiness is often a shield or camouflage for the beauty that lies within. The Balinese showed me that finding joy is not about masking our view of the mess in our lives or covering our ears from the noise surrounding us. It's about staring and listening more intently, so we can see the beauty in the clutter and hear music in the commotion. Happiness is not about searching for and obtaining something that is missing, but rather about fully examining and appreciating what is already found.

Someone I admired and lost to lung cancer shared that the disease caused him to "distinguish the meaningful from the mundane." He was right. Any form of suffering causes us to adjust our priorities in life. Big events in our lives and the people we love have a way of reminding us what really matters. But life is also full of small moments—the chores—that fill our days. It's easy to label those as distractions or interruptions to our lives. But they too are moments to treasure. It is the little things, the ordinary things, that make us feel normal. And, when everything feels uncertain, normalcy feels pretty incredible.

My memories of my past brought me peace. The support of others gave me strength. With only one round of immunotherapy complete, I knew I still had a long journey ahead. But I didn't dwell on the road in front of me. Instead, I laughed at my daughters' silly jokes and smiled while folding the laundry with Tonya.

Slowly, slowly. I savored the gift I was given—an ordinary day.

SECTION 2

LEARN

"Live as if you were to die tomorrow.
Learn as if you were to live forever."

– Mahatma Gandhi

Being given the gift of life comes with the responsibility of staying curious about things in our lives. Whether learning about the stars in the universe, keeping informed with the news, or reading a good book, learning isn't just the food that nourishes our minds, it is the fuel that drives a brighter future—for our short lifetimes and for the generations that follow.

I want to...

- ❖ Stay informed and committed to issues that matter.
- ❖ Gain insight, understanding, and skills on new topics and subject areas.
- ❖ Design, build, and create solutions that improve others' lives.
- ❖ Understand and appreciate different cultures and perspectives.
- ❖ Share my limited knowledge and skills with others.

Examples of things that help me learn...

- ❖ Reading a good book.
- ❖ Thinking about how seemingly unrelated topics relate to each other.
- ❖ Listening to others and seeing how different perspectives and others' strengths make ideas stronger and open the world to more interesting and rewarding possibilities.
- ❖ Reading and listening to the news from several different sources.
- ❖ Struggling with a problem until I find or develop a solution.
- ❖ Traveling to other parks, cities, states, and countries to experience the beauty of different places and people.

CHAPTER 10:

WRESTLING WITH THE TRUTH

Life Lesson: Let's fight for the truth. Let's also use the truth in our fights.

WHEN I WAS A KID, my friends and I loved to watch professional wrestling. Some of my favorite wrestlers included the Macho Man Randy Savage, the Ultimate Warrior, and Hulk Hogan. Wrestlers like Jake the Snake didn't fight fair, lied, were mean and insulting, and, well, carried a snake. Hulk Hogan, on the other hand, was charismatic, honest, funny, and stood up to bullies. When wrestlers like them met in the ring, it wasn't just a battle between two muscle men. It was a battle of good versus evil.

Many of my friends insisted the fighting was real. I was skeptical. I loved the action as much as any fifth grader, but some of their punches didn't seem to land and the "figure four leg-lock" just didn't look as painful as the muscle-bound men seemed to let on. Nonetheless, when a group of these professional wrestlers decided to perform (or fight, depending on your perspective) in my hometown high school gym,

I wanted to be there. The men who came weren't the biggest-named wrestlers, but seeing guys battle over good versus evil wasn't something I wanted to miss. I don't remember much about the matches, but I'm pretty sure the good guy won because that was the way the world worked then; good triumphed over evil. What I do remember most is what I saw when leaving. All the wrestlers, the same guys who were screaming into mics about each other and breaking boards over each other's heads, all climbed into a Greyhound bus laughing and talking together.

My friends and I may have disagreed about the authenticity of what we witnessed during their match, but we all agreed how thrilling the action was to watch. I also was willing to let reality slip away for entertainment. I *wanted* the characters to be real and rationalized that true fights occasionally did happen. Who knew… Maybe they were rumbling in the aisle of their shared Greyhound bus all the way home. (I didn't have evidence of any bus brawls, but I also didn't have evidence it *didn't* happen.)

My joy for the spectacle of the sport continued even when I was older. As a senior in high school, some friends of mine and I decided to pretend to be WWE wrestlers as a skit in a pep session for our basketball team. I played the character of Macho Man Randy Savage (I wanted to include the mascot name, so my stage name was technically the "Ranger Savage"). Our act included breakable boards, a chainsaw, and our school's state-champion wrestler who entered the ring on a cable and pulley that we secretly installed from the top bleachers to the center of the ring. Our little WWE event that started out as a skit during a pep session became the main event open to the public the night before sectional to build enthusiasm for the entire community.

At the beginning of our skit, the character Jim "the Hacksaw" Duggan started an old smoky chainsaw and raced around the ring before the match started. The alarmed referee instructed him that chainsaws are forbidden in the fight. Unfazed, Duggan charged after the referee and both men disappeared behind the ring. We simulated his body being sawed into pieces and tossed a mannequin's legs, arms, torso (dressed as a referee), and head onto the ring. Two other classmates, playing the role of EMTs, raced out with a stretcher and started picking up the body parts. Although some in the crowd probably averted their young kids' eyes in horror, most cheered and laughed at the spectacle we had orchestrated.

My own personal favorite memory of that moment—indeed of the entire skit—was what the audience never heard and a line that wasn't scripted. My English teacher, Rock Emmert, who played the role of Hulk Hogan approached the EMTs with a worried expression as they were setting the referee's body parts on the stretcher. Still in character, he bemoaned: "He's going to be okay, right?"

Stepping away from reality at times can be entertaining, relaxing, and even productive. After all, our basketball team ended up winning their first sectional the year of our wrestling skit. But the fun in fictional acts, plays, movies, or novels usually lies in knowing the plot is not real—that everything will be okay despite the horror we might see. We are comforted knowing that the world really isn't filled with guys who fight with a chainsaw and a snake. If at any point we become too emotionally entangled in the battle, we can simply change the channel.

I wish life were that simple. In addition to the physical, financial, and emotional toll that comes with a cancer diagnosis, I wasn't prepared for the practical intellectual challenges that also came with the disease. When I felt the worst and our family was the most vulnerable emotionally, I faced some of the most important decisions of my life—decisions that really were a matter of life and death.

The amount of information I received from so many sources was overwhelming. Since my original diagnosis, I had been receiving advice from family, friends, and complete strangers on treatment options. Taking CBD oil, avoiding sugar, visiting Jerusalem, rubbing my stomach with holy water, eating a special kind of dog food, and just maintaining a positive attitude—these suggestions and many more were some of the treatment methods people swore worked for others. I just had to believe too.

I was skeptical.

Cancer has a way of hiding from the body's immune system. PD-L1, a protein found on some normal cells, can also attach to cancer cells. This can cause our immune system to mistakenly recognize cancer cells as healthy cells and not attack it. The goal of immunotherapy is to prevent that from happening. It tries to keep PD-L1 from attaching to the cancer so our immune system knows to go after it. In order to be eligible for immunotherapy, Dr. Helft and his team tested the cancer cells in my stomach to see if they contained PD-L1 proteins. They did. So, the treatment had the *possibility* of working. It also had the possibility of attacking the healthy organs and tissues in my body.

So, although it was my best shot, I was skeptical.

I tried to find the latest research online and wanted to find the loophole, a way out of the grasp of the disease that perhaps others had failed to find in the past. As I digested information about T-cells, checkpoint inhibitors, and a general overview of the immune system and immunotherapy treatments, the most important discovery I came to realize was how little I knew about all of this.

I was not going to become an oncologist in the course of a few weeks. It became clear that I didn't need to know deeply about PD-L1, T-cell proliferation, or microRNA. What I really needed wasn't answers to all my questions about the genetics of my cancer or the science behind the latest advances in cancer treatment. I needed to know who to trust.

I knew I couldn't do this on my own. And, although I loved and appreciated all my family members, friends, and strangers' concern and their well-intentioned advice, I decided that I would have to trust my doctors and a few close family members, such as Tonya, for the truth and for making difficult decisions.

The most important decision that needed to be answered after my diagnosis was what hospital and doctors to use. Although Tonya and I had studied and considered going to other out-of-state hospitals, we ultimately decided to put our trust in Dr. Helft as my oncologist and the team at Indiana University Health.

Tonya and I considered several factors when deciding who to trust with my care. Certainly, there were practical factors. Having the Indiana University Simon Cancer Center only thirty minutes from home meant a portion of our lives (living arrangements, being with our girls, continuing to work) wouldn't be as disrupted compared to going to other out-of-state hospitals. Certainly, we also considered the hospital's reputation for cancer treatment and the financial weight of our decisions. However, Dr. Helft's willingness to see himself as a learner was what impressed me the most.

From the moment he introduced himself as my oncologist, Dr. Helft struck me as the perfect partner in helping chart the best path of care. He was kind, compassionate, thoughtful, informed, and honest. In one of my first visits, he asked how much information he should share about my situation, explaining that some patients prefer to know as much as possible about their diagnosis and prognosis (information about the progression of their disease, what to expect from a treatment, options to consider), but others do better with less information. I definitely wanted to be as informed as possible.

So with each visit, not only would Dr. Helft openly share what he was seeing from medical tests, he would tell me his thoughts on what it likely meant and what he was considering to provide me the best care possible. He also listened. He wanted to know how I was feeling, what questions I had, and better understand any of my concerns. Although he was considered a national expert in treating cancer, his knowledge wasn't what impressed me most, it was his humble admission of what he *didn't* know. He was constantly learning. Unlike some other doctors who I'd encountered in the past, he didn't flex his knowledge or pretend to be the keeper of all the right answers. He welcomed and encouraged me to receive second opinions of the best treatment options.

Dr. Helft blended optimism with candor and was endlessly patient with my questions. Even though my sparse knowledge of human anatomy and cancer treatment were readily apparent in our conversations, he would respectfully discuss the logic behind his recommendations. He seemed to genuinely appreciate me challenging his reasoning on how to best apply his knowledge to my situation. He acknowledged, despite the growing body of cancer research and advances in medicine, that most options came with differing degrees of certainty. He was as hopeful and as optimistic as anyone I've met. But, when faced with new findings that didn't quite match his hopes or expectations, he too could become skeptical.

So, I am a skeptic, Dr. Helft is a skeptic, and most people I know consider themselves skeptical of others opinions and ideas. I've realized there are two types of skepticism: *experimentally* skeptical versus *rigidly* skeptical. One is productive. One is not.

Being experimentally skeptical requires one to test their ideas and existing knowledge against new ideas and information. New arguments supported by evidence and backed by sound reasoning causes us to further lean into our position or rethink our own ideas. In an experimentally skeptical mind, nothing is fully settled. We watch the tug-of-war of ideas pull against each other and allow our minds to nudge with the arguments with the most strength. Although we may never reach one hundred percent certainty on any topic, we become increasingly confident of an idea the further the red marker in the middle is pulled in one direction. Being experimentally skeptical makes us curious. Curiosity leads to learning, to understanding, to appreciation, to growth, to innovation, to truth.

Being rigidly skeptical is the opposite. Those who are rigidly skeptical reject new ideas and new information that doesn't reinforce the position they already hold. Everything is already settled. Opinions quickly morph into indisputable truths. Little will cause the rigidly skeptical person to change their mind. They are one hundred percent certain. They watch a tug-of-war of ideas cheering only for one side and walk away convinced that if the red marker doesn't go in the direction of their side, the other side must have cheated. Being rigidly skeptical makes us cynical. Cynicalism leads to ignorance, to denial, to stagnation, to hatred, to lies.

Every day we make decisions: what to have for breakfast, how fast to drive, what light bulbs to buy, and (in some instances) choosing what treatments to take to best address a disease. How we choose to make our decisions is based on our experience, our goals, and whether to be experimentally skeptical or rigidly skeptical. Eating bacon and eggs may bring us strength and satisfaction (in the short term) but also higher cholesterol (in the long run). Driving fast may get us to a destination quicker but also increases our chances of killing someone. Choosing an LED light bulb may cost us more at the checkout counter but also reduces greenhouse emissions from power plants. Cancer treatment may extend life but also reduce quality of life. These, along with millions of decisions big and small, are our choices. Each path we choose to follow may fundamentally alter our destination for ourselves and others.

We *should* be skeptical of anyone who tells us what to think or do, whether that's someone who claims professional wrestling is or isn't real or someone who claims one form of treatment is better than another. But let's not mistake being experimentally skeptical with rigidly skeptical. Being the former means we are dismissive *regardless* of the credibility of the person or merit of the information shared, whereas being the latter means we accept and act on the information precisely *because* of the credibility of the person and the merit of the information shared. Being rigidly skeptical *insulates* us in a fictional world we want to be true; being experimentally skeptical *empowers* us to create the best world possible. The person who tells me (without evidence) I should eat bacon every day, drive as fast as I want, buy the cheapest light bulbs possible, and drink beer to fight off cancer may have the guidance I *wish* were true, but the consequences of my actions (or inactions) will undoubtedly be controlled by what *is* true.

Separating fact from fiction is difficult. We are increasingly living in parallel realities propped up by news feeds, advertisements, and entertainment designed to keep our attention, provoke emotions, and sell us products. Social media is becoming echo chambers where people shout their own version of a reality to those who already agree with them. Conspiracy theories continue to gain traction and false information is quickly adopted as evidence.

We must choose our form of skepticism wisely. The truth still matters. Sharing a common set of facts matters. If we cannot agree to basic truths or even such a thing as truth, we will never agree to opinions on the best way to solve the problems that confront us—whether the topic is global warming, election fraud, pandemics, or personal health decisions. As Nobel Laureate and chemist Harold Kroto stated, "I think the most important thing that young people should be taught at school is how they can decide what they're being told is true."

Listening to a WWE wrestler scream nonsense about their competitor may be entertaining, but believing the words of leaders spewing lies is damaging and dangerous. The good news is that we have a choice.

We have agency. We aren't characters in George Orwell's dystopian society portrayed in *1984*. But, every time we click a link online recommended for us, like a post, or share a comment or resource, we must recognize the engine driving this information is not intended to inform or thoughtfully guide us. Every time we accept the false narrative of politicians, news organizations, or anyone spreading misinformation, we all take one step closer to that dystopian society where "The past was erased, the erasure was forgotten, the lie became the truth."

The key to unraveling the truth begins with being curious. We must be willing to admit we don't have all the answers and embrace our willingness to learn from others. We must become better at using skepticism as a guide, not a barrier, for being convinced. These were the very qualities that made Dr. Helft a trusted partner in my care and the attributes I tried to mimic as his patient.

Choosing the right doctors or even the best treatment didn't guarantee success for my healing, but it did increase my odds. So, with an open heart and earnest mind, I knew we would let scientific research, Dr. Helft's experience and expertise, my tolerance and goals for treatment, and our collective reasoning skills guide our next move.

I still didn't know if my archenemy, cancer, would piledrive me into the mat or throw me out of the ring. When receiving the news of my diagnosis, I felt like my entire life had been sawed to pieces. But thanks to scientists and doctors who had continued to ask better questions and seek better answers, immunotherapy was giving me a chance.

So perhaps Rock, in the role of Hulk Hogan, was right. Maybe the truth was that everything would be okay and our family and I could be made whole again.

CHAPTER 11:

THE LOVE OF LOGIC

Life Lesson: *Both calculus and life have their limits.*

AFTER A FEW MORE ROUNDS of chemotherapy and immunotherapy, I stopped chemo and continued only with immunotherapy every three weeks. After about six more rounds of treatment, Dr. Helft scheduled another PET/CT scan for me. Overall, I was feeling really good—much better than I had for some time. I didn't know if that was an indication of the treatment working as designed or just some temporary relief from the adverse side effects of chemo. The PET/CT scan would soon tell us whether my situation was stabilizing or getting worse.

It was early January, a time when Christmas trees—a symbol of life, rebirth, and stamina—are boxed up in basements or are abruptly tossed to the curb for recycling. The glow of Christmas lights no longer instilled a sense of brightness, hope, and good in the world; they instead only served as reminders of a joyous occasion and celebration already passed. I was eager to say goodbye to 2018 but also feared 2019 may very well be the year etched on my gravestone.

Tonya and I nervously sat in one of the patient rooms waiting for Dr. Helft. We were hoping for slowed growth and even reductions in both the size and intensity of tumor and lymph node activity that had shown up on previous scans. Dr. Helft entered the room with his normal warm smile. He asked how I was feeling then transitioned to the results he knew we were waiting to hear. "Look, I'm not sure what to make of your scan right now," he said with a concerned expression, adding, "Let me show you."

He brought up an image on the computer screen. It was my scan—lit up like the stale Christmas lights that had outlasted their usefulness. He continued with an empathetic tone. "It looks like the tumor in your stomach has grown in size. There also is increased activity in your lymph nodes in your abdomen area—which are likely indications of it spreading." He paused, trying to be optimistic but remain honest and factual. "It's possible—but unlikely—that the increased size and activity is a side effect of immunotherapy. But a more likely explanation is that the cancer is not responding to the immunotherapy treatment."

The analytical portion of my personality once again pushed away the emotional side. I asked for clarification on some of the specifics, wanting to know the precise measurements of the growth and anatomy of the areas of increased activity, jotting notes on my phone. We continued to talk as if I was a new medical intern learning how to read a scan for the first time. I focused on the screen hoping again that finding the right question or the right set of numbers from the results might somehow allow him and me to form a different conclusion.

Dr. Helft explained how he wanted their team to surgically get a better look inside my abdomen and biopsy the area lighting up the scans. However, if what he expected was confirmed, there really weren't any other alternative treatment strategies. I would probably be asked to go back on chemo, which in addition to being difficult to tolerate had not been very effective in treating other gastric cancer patients. I wasn't sure that was a path I wanted to retrace.

When I finally paused in my questioning, I looked away from the screen to Tonya, who sat with her head down. This wasn't just some academic conversation about some John Doe patient, I realized, and my disappointment, frustration, and grief began to overtake me. I walked away into the bathroom and began to sob. Immunotherapy was our Plan A. We had no Plan B.

Did it even make sense to do the surgery and get a biopsy? Going off treatment meant imminent death—probably a matter of a few months. Going on chemo meant possibly some prolonged time—a few more months, but the quality of my life would be worse. Immunotherapy was my only hope. So, if it wasn't working… Well, I really needed that plan B.

Over the next several days, I thought about my options. I tried to dissect the information in my head as if it was a math problem. A mathematical modeling class I took in college tried to reduce everyday decisions into a quantifiable way of knowing which choice to make. For example, whether to carry an umbrella on a given day was about putting a value to different options and outcomes—getting wet, carrying an umbrella unnecessarily, the chance of rain, et cetera—and then crunching through a formula to spit out the clear choice to make.

Perhaps decisions on my health care could also be reduced to a similar model—only the stakes were much higher.

As I tried to mathematically unravel the mystery of whether to continue with the surgery in my head, I couldn't help but laugh at myself. I thought about our girls again. My thoughts faded to a memory of us sitting at a whiteboard when they were probably just five and seven years old—with me trying to turn a simple idea into a lesson on mathematics and logic.

"A square *is* a rectangle," I declared with delight as I started to draw the shape on the whiteboard in front of them. It was a true statement. A rectangle has four sides and four right angles. So, any polygon (or using Lizzie's language: a shape that has no holes and no curvy sides) with exactly four sides and four right angles must be a rectangle. Ergo, a square is a rectangle. I then added with great mystery and excitement, "But a rectangle is not necessarily a square."

Anna Mae and Lizzie didn't seem impressed or convinced. They knew the shape of a circle, a square, and a rectangle. I asked them to show me the difference. So, they grabbed the whiteboard marker and drew all three shapes and declared as if they were teaching me this time, "Daddy, this one is a rectangle. This one is a square."

"But *why* is that one a rectangle?" I said, trying to reel them in. They looked at each other as if they were questioning whether or not I had ever learned my shapes. I paused, realizing this must feel like some technical nuance of language only math nerds care about and that would only confuse them learning the properties of basic shapes.

But I began to convince myself that this wasn't a lesson on shapes at all. It was a lesson on mathematical reasoning, on problem-solving, on logic—on starting with a few rules or assumptions and building a whole world of conclusions. So when I saw the window of opportunity open slightly for spreading my love of mathematics and logic to my daughters, I dove through head first.

In mathematics, postulates are the basic assumptions that are accepted as true. For example, in geometry, postulate one states that through any two points, there is exactly one line. This postulate was scribbled on some papyrus by Euclid in 300 BC. The basic truths or assumptions are the seeds from which enormous mathematical forests grew. Using only a few basic assumptions, philosophers and mathematicians were able to conclude a few more things, which allowed them to prove something else, which in turn allowed us to determine another thing, opening the door for the next generation to form the next conclusion, and so on. It's like a Rube Goldberg machine that keeps propelling the next act. A marble rolls down a ramp that strikes a domino which falls onto a switch that lights a match that causes air to fill a balloon… Only the mathematical machine never comes to an end, with each stunt becoming more complex than the one before.

This is why I loved math and why I wanted my girls to love math. For me, it has never been about algorithms or contrived steps that march you from point A to D. It's about knowing that you have a bag of tools—tricks, really—that if applied accurately and appropriately, allow you to discover your next destination. Mathematicians don't just solve problems, they uncover opportunities.

Mathematics is the language of the universe. It gives us a way to understand our surroundings, quantify relationships, and predict our future. Much like a parent who determines whether their toddler is tall by looking at a pediatric growth chart, mathematics allows us to understand our best options during difficult health situations.

Mathematics told a story about my diagnosis and prognosis without ever muttering a word. It's easy to dispute opinions and even question the intentions of others. It's easy to become enamored by anecdotal success stories or feel threatened or scared from situations gone badly. But mathematics doesn't care who you are or who you want to be. It is a faceless friend with a steady hand that delivers the truth—even when it hurts.

After Dr. Helft explained the results of the PET/CT scan, I finally asked him the cliché question that had been in my head, but I never had the courage to voice. "If immunotherapy isn't working, how long do I have left?"

His first response was a question back: "Do you really want to know?"

Reluctantly, I assured him that I did. He sympathetically explained that the average untreated survival of metastatic gastric cancer is four to six months after the diagnosis. Left untreated, my odds of living more than a couple years would be zero percent. Without treatment, my fate was sealed. He also explained that the average *treated* survival period wasn't a lot better—about twelve months. The five-year survival rate for treated patients was about four percent. Neither option felt very promising.

I also knew that given the recent breakthroughs in cancer research, these stats largely did not account for possibilities that came with immunotherapy—but that was *only if* my body would respond to it. My PET/CT scan showed growth and increased activity, so the logical conclusion was that cancer was spreading and growing—and not responding to the treatment. And if it was growing and spreading, I really had limited time remaining. Mathematics always left room for what was possible, but it was honest and direct enough to inform me on what is most probable.

I'm not sure I ever did convince Anna Mae and Lizzie that day at the whiteboard that logic forces us to accept that a square is a special kind of rectangle. And really, my bigger lesson was that logic teaches us that our conclusions are based on some definitions or assumptions. Logic reminds us that in every argument or nearly everything we hold to be true, there are assumptions.

Time and time again, we've learned that what seems obvious and certain based on our individual perspectives may not end up fitting the perspective of others, the beliefs of the next generation, or even the facts that we've yet to discover. Logic is like dominos standing in a row with each domino completely reliant on the one that precedes it. Place one domino a little out of position and the dominos that follow will remain standing. Introduce faulty logic along your path of mathematical discovery and everything that follows is erroneous.

Galileo and a few other scientists before him had the courage to question if Earth was the center of the universe. Albert Einstein challenged some of Isaac Newton's assumptions and showed that Newton's Laws of Motion were only approximately correct, falling apart when objects approached the speed of light. And, accepting some different postulates in geometry ultimately led to plausible alternatives, giving shape to non-Euclidean geometries like elliptical geometry and hyperbolic geometry.

So, although logic allows us to build on our assumptions to discover new ideas and stronger arguments, it forces us to acknowledge the vulnerabilities of our thoughts. Oftentimes, something can seem obvious and absolute—like the sun appearing to circle Earth—until one day it is proven wrong.

With the results of my PET/CT scan and dim survival rate numbers in hand, now more than ever, I hoped Anna Mae and Lizzie would ultimately learn a lesson not only about the precision and predictability of mathematics, but the uncertainty and flaws in conclusions based on assumptions.

CHAPTER 12:

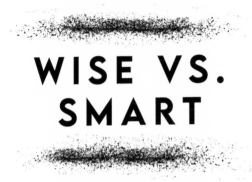

WISE VS. SMART

Life Lesson: Let that old dog teach you new tricks.

As MUCH AS I WANTED to make sense of the world and of my situation by plotting numbers on a graph, finding my best course of treatment wasn't just a heady exercise in determining and staying on the longest path—especially if that extra mileage only further exhausted those carrying me through a dark and dense jungle. As my family and I navigated this disease together and my options for treatment, I needed to not just make smart decisions, but wise ones.

If immunotherapy wasn't working, I speculated that my doctors would probably ask me to go back on chemotherapy. To most, it was the smart choice: the one that made the most sense medically and statistically. Chemo wouldn't provide me a cure for my cancer, but it might slow the spread—at least temporarily—giving me more time. The next round of treatment would probably be the hard stuff, a combination of drugs that would be much more difficult to tolerate. So, although chemo might extend my life, I wasn't sure if that was really living. Was going off treatment perhaps not as smart—medically speaking—but wiser because it meant a better quality of life with the time remaining?

As I thought about that distinction, I also thought about both Anna Mae and Lizzie's future, imagining them graduating from college—an occasion that I most likely would not get to attend.

Shortly after I graduated from college, I started my first job as a math teacher in Monticello, Indiana, about thirty minutes north of West Lafayette, the home of the Purdue Boilermakers. Although I completed my undergraduate degree at Ball State, some of my friends still had a semester of schooling to complete at Purdue. Since I was looking for a place to live, I jumped at the chance to become roommates with one of my best friends from high school, Scott, and some other equally entertaining and nice guys I knew.

Even before I moved in, I was pleasantly surprised to learn that Scott's dog would also be my roommate. Bosco, or Sco Dog as I frequently called him, was a big Staffordshire terrier with a smooth coat that looked like it was carefully designed and painted by an artist. He was mostly white with patches of black and dark brown that resembled the coat of a tiger. The small black spot over his right eye made him look like a thoughtful, attentive listener among friends and a no-nonsense, fierce fighter with those he viewed as threats.

Although we introduced him as Scott's pet to others, that never quite accurately described his hierarchy in the apartment. Bosco was like a lion in a jungle. He was king of the apartment, ruler of all who entered his space. His room—or perhaps more accurately, his throne—was the most prominent feature of the small apartment. The moment you entered the front door, you couldn't help but notice a carefully crafted hole in the wall that functioned as the doorway for Bosco's living quarters. Just in case the gaping hole didn't catch your attention, ceramic flooring led into his humble home and a painted image of a house, complete with a mailbox, adorned his entryway. We all hailed Bosco. I was partially convinced that Scott went into construction engineering in order to have sufficient skills to build Bosco a proper palace in the apartment.

Bosco's overall size, rounded face, thick neck, wide shoulders, and deep bark could be intimidating to others at times. But his calm demeanor, soulful gazes, and attentive nature made him impossible not to love. He had become one of the guys, packing on more than the "freshman 15"—living the lazy and luxurious life of eating too much, drinking too much, and sleeping too much. On weekday mornings, when I woke early to get ready to go to my teaching job, I would find Sco Dog lying on his back on the sofa (the same sofa he was not supposed to sit on) with a pillow tucked under his head, his paws dangling off to the side. His big belly would swell with the inhale and exhale of his deep breaths, like a human who had fallen asleep watching TV. When I would turn on a light in the kitchen to make my way around the apartment, Bosco would open one eye, look at me with annoyance, and roll over on his side to return to his deep breathing.

He was mild-mannered and seemed content watching basketball and episodes of *Friends* with us. The only indication of his inner beast was when he was given his special treat, a roasted pig ear. When he had his snack within reach, all bets were off. Even if you stepped in his direction while he was mauling on his pig ear, his soft dark-brown eyes would immediately transform into a deadly stare, and his snout would tighten to reveal his strong teeth, and he would give one of the coldest, deepest throaty growls. Regardless how much he loved you, if you tried to interfere with his pig ear moment, he would have no choice but to kill you.

Bosco provided both comradery and entertainment to us and anyone who would visit. He seemed to understand everything we said and marveled everyone with his ability to follow our commands. Sure, he may have gotten a Doritos bag stuck on his head once, but we didn't see that as a lapse in intellect as much as the challenge that comes from having a big head and lack of thumbs.

We liked to show off his talents. We could place a dog biscuit on top of his snout and give the command "stay." He would sit frozen with deep concentration in his eyes as if the biscuit would explode like a small bomb should it strike the floor. He would sit there for literally minutes sometimes, with slobber dripping from his mouth, and the biscuit resting motionless on his snout. And then with the simple words "get it," Bosco would shake his head and snatch the biscuit midair in his jaws, making it disappear like a magician.

One of our proudest moments came on a Saturday when we finally completed the difficult challenge of teaching Bosco how to get us a beer from the refrigerator. We put a rope around the door handle of the refrigerator, and upon giving the command, "Open the fridge, Bosco!" he would go to the refrigerator, tilt his big head sideways, clench the rope in his jaws, and back up, pulling open the refrigerator door.

Then, he would stand by the refrigerator waiting for the second command: "Bring a beer, Bosco." With that, Bosco would put his thick head into the refrigerator, tilt it sideways, and grab a bottle of beer from the side, and with concentration in his eyes and pride radiating from his wagging tail, he would bring us our slobbery beer. In truth, the trick was rarely performed with perfection and frequently didn't go as planned. Lots of times the beer would get knocked over in the refrigerator or dropped on the way back to us. Yet when he pulled off the stunt, it was magical. We would toast to our Sco Dog for a job well done.

Bosco was a genius. And in truth, we were pretty proud of ourselves too. We only imagined what else our Dog Wonder might be able to do for us. Who knows, maybe he also would be able to clean those dishes stacking up in the sink with his pristine tongue. We went out that night to celebrate our impressive accomplishment (and, well, because we celebrated every Saturday night). We all had a little extra bounce in our step and wider grins on our faces because we had done something special. Something brilliant. We had taught Bosco how to get us a beer!

We made our way back to the apartment at the end of our evening out. Even though I'd already had my fill of beer for the night, I found myself wanting another one, just to see Sco Dog work his magic. *Brilliant. We are brilliant!*

When we opened the door, we were shocked to see a mess scattered across the living room and kitchen floor. We weren't necessarily a tidy group, but this was different. It looked like we were ransacked.

Pieces of raw meat, smashed eggs, an empty pizza box, and wrappings from bacon and sausage were spread across the floor like confetti. We stood at the doorway staring, confused. And then we saw it, the clue that unraveled the mystery: The refrigerator door was wide open.

We called for Bosco. Instead of greeting us with his normal enthusiasm, he slumbered out of his cave sheepishly, with his tail between his legs and regret in his eyes. Bosco had eaten just about everything in the refrigerator and left the trail of his night of gluttony in the kitchen and throughout the living room.

I said the same words that ran through my head only moments before we entered the apartment, only this time with sarcasm. "Brilliant. We are brilliant." I took stock of the mess in front of us. "I don't think we thought this through. We taught a dog how to open the refrigerator."

My undergraduate work included multiple courses in calculus, differential equations, statistics, mathematical modeling, abstract geometry, and various courses in psychology and education. I graduated summa cum laude. My roommates and friends were about to also graduate from Purdue with an impressive resume of various engineering, math, physics, and construction courses, internships, and experiences under their belt. Only a few months before, I had stood in my cap and gown, with someone giving a speech about my future. We were the ones that were going to create a better world for everyone. And yet, here I stood shoulder to shoulder with the faces of the future in a wrecked apartment with an empty refrigerator and a fat dog.

We were supposed to be the smart ones. We certainly were not wise.

Smart means different things to different people. I think of smart as a mixture of what you know and your ability to learn something new. There are people who are labeled smart because of test scores, academic achievements, or other qualities that get associated with formal education. Others are labeled smart because of their reasoning skills, intuitive way of solving problems, and ability to deal with new or difficult situations, or what often gets called street smarts. As a society, we even try to quantify one's cognitive aptitude with a manufactured intelligence quotient or IQ. However, the word *smart* often doesn't account for drive and effort or other forms of intelligence, like emotional intelligence.

Wisdom, on the other hand, is about judgment and decision making. It's about doing what is right. Wisdom considers past experiences, sensitivity to others, and ethical and moral factors, and relies on your brain and your heart. Being smart and wise are not mutually exclusive, but the following chart explains how I see them as different:

	SMART PERSON	WISE PERSON
Disagreeing with a person	Uses facts, logic, and data to make their case in hopes of winning the argument	Listens carefully and attentively with an open mind in hopes of finding common ground and the best way forward
Finding a Solution	Uses algorithms, science, and math to find the right answer	Considers assumptions, biases, and other factors that are inherent in calculations and wants to consider multiple solutions to a problem

Being in a Relationship	Wants to be right	Wants to be respectful
Raising a Child	Values good grades, high achievement, and top diplomas	Values effort, progress, kindness, empathy, collaboration, and curiosity
Negotiating	Sees it as a zero-sum game—one person will gain from the other person's losses	Sees it as an opportunity for mutual benefit and establishing strong long-term relationships
Decisions are Made	With their brain	Both with their brain and their heart
Frequently Ask	What is optimal?	What is right?

As a person with stage 4 stomach cancer, I thought a lot about my own life. I reflected on my accomplishments and my failures, on life's moments that brought me joy and experiences that brought me sorrow. Cancer certainly did not make me smarter. In fact, when I was undergoing chemotherapy, I had difficulty processing the simplest of concepts, and everything I read, listened to, or watched felt overwhelming. (Chemo brain, a common term used by cancer survivors to describe thinking and memory problems that can occur during and after cancer treatment, is a real thing.) And yet, my struggle has made me more sensitive to other people's suffering, grateful for my many blessings, and more attuned to what is really important in life. I certainly won't claim to be a wise man, but I do believe that my suffering, heightened realization of my mortality, and the love that I have seen in others have made me a little wiser.

College (and formal education in general) is great at challenging us intellectually. We are tested by others on what we do and don't know.

But in life, we face a different, but more important test. We are tested by deciding *what to do* with what we know and how to face what we don't know.

We should commit to being learners forever. No, I am not suggesting that recent graduates must enroll in more classes. (At some point, I think their parents will want them to get a job.) I am simply challenging all of us to see ourselves as a learner in all situations. But more importantly, I hope recent graduates—and really everyone—will strive not just to become smarter, but to become wiser. Sure, some brilliant ideas will turn out messy, like a dog trick that goes amok. Life will still hand out surprises, like a terminal disease that turns the world upside down. But even when staring into the shatters of what was once whole, it is the wisdom of others that will bring joy, laughter, comfort, and peace with what remains.

CHAPTER 13:

HAVE FAITH

Life Lesson: God is good, but good God, can we all be good too?!

I DECIDED TO PROCEED WITH the outpatient surgery Dr. Helft had suggested. The plan was to remove one of my lymph nodes, to laparoscopically look to see if tumors were on the outside of my stomach and present on other organs, and to biopsy the tissue samples. When I sat in the room with the nurse preparing me for the procedure, she asked if I had any questions or concerns. I flatly replied, "It's not the procedure that scares me. It's the results."

When the nurse left the room, I sat quietly with Tonya next to me. I thought of the words of advice that so many had shared with me since my diagnosis and would repeat with each new challenge: "have faith." They were words that made me feel mixed emotions. I was incredibly touched by how many people—friends, family, and complete strangers—said they were praying for me. I also prayed each night with my kids and gave thanks for each new morning. That ritual—those prayers—did seem to help. The strength from others thinking of me did bring me strength. And, my own prayers seemed to bring me a peace and comfort that I couldn't quite explain.

And yet, something about those two simple words—"have faith"—bothered me and still bothers me today. I want to believe. In an all-powerful God. That He has a plan for me. That everything happened for a reason. That His Son was born of the Virgin Mary and died so that I might live forever. That everything will be okay. I want to believe in all those things. I'm just not sure that I do.

I struggle to find such certainty that seems to come naturally to others. Tonya and I grew up Catholic. Both of our kids were baptized as Catholics. Although faith remains an important part of my life and our family life, I'm not sure I can call myself Catholic because there is a fair amount about the Catholic faith that I question and I rarely attend church. And yet, there is also so much my faith, my religion, has taught and given my family and me. As much as I want to write a story for my kids that ultimately gives a lesson about the power of God and in believing, the truth is that I'm confused and conflicted—not just in what I want my kids to know, but about what I have learned from religion versus what I actually believe. My faith ultimately remains a journey, rather than a destination.

In writing this, I genuinely am trying to search for the truth. Admitting my vulnerabilities and my religious uncertainty—especially at a time when I may soon stand in front of my maker—feels both frightening and foolish. I recognize this should be the time that I am citing my unwavering belief that Jesus Christ is my Savior. After all, my window of opportunity for doing so is quickly closing. Also, I certainly don't want to use my limited time to alienate those who love me most. But it is also precisely because of that love that I feel the urge to write about my beliefs in an effort to understand them myself, my earnest desire to continue to learn and grow from others, and to bring myself closer to the mystery I call God.

I don't pretend to have the answers. I'm not sure I even know the right questions. But these are among the ones I frequently ask myself:

❖ **What is faith?**

For me, faith is ultimately about accepting that which has not—and maybe cannot—be proven. As a result, I often associate faith more with feelings than facts. As I've shared, I'm a person who values scientific proof, historical context, logic, hard facts, and sound reasoning. And so, the notion of accepting or even entertaining ideas and making claims based on feelings or that which cannot be proven seems fundamentally fallible. And yet, denying that which is unproven—especially when it comes to religious views—feels like I'm also being alienating, rebellious, and blasphemous. I also fully admit how little I know about the makings of our world or our beings. So with that admission, I feel that I also must remain open to the idea that there are forces around me and feelings within me that are real, yet mysterious. There is both peace and power that comes from succumbing and accepting that which we do not know, yet believe. After all, practically speaking, we all put our faith in something or someone every day. When I get into my car, I am putting faith in the other drivers—accepting that their behavior is not within my control. I *have faith* that they won't accidentally or deliberately crash into me. Likewise, although I cannot prove it or even fully explain it, I also have faith that there is something bigger than me—than all of us—something I cannot touch or see, but remains with me nonetheless.

❖ What do I love about my faith?

My faith brings me gratitude, peace, comfort, strength, and hope. In addition to my private prayers, I treasured my shared prayers with my daughters at night when they were younger. The structure of our prayers was typically the same. We thanked God for our many blessings, asked Him to look after those in need, and then shared areas that we personally needed support, comfort, or healing. For those who don't believe in God, I know this exercise can seem awkward or even silly. Yes, the logical person in me struggles to imagine a bearded man in the sky taking notes of my words then shifting to the role of puppet master to orchestrate events based on my input lying with my kids talking to Him that night.

And yet, although I cannot explain the power of prayer, I know that I feel it. So, my only reaction and advice to others is that whether you believe in God or not, I highly recommend a similar ritual to anyone. Even if your ritual is an exercise in mindfulness or meditation, rather than prayer, there is incredible power and comfort that comes from being purposely and deliberately focused on others' well-being, for acknowledging and even embracing our worries, and to reflect on all that is good. Regardless of my state of mind entering a prayer, I always exit the prayer feeling a greater sense of peace and comfort. There is something about knowing I am never alone, that there is a being, a power or force larger than me, that is humbling and empowering. Submitting that I am not in control of all my circumstances is not about surrendering my role in matters. Rather, it's about fully seeing my role with greater perspective.

I am also amazed by the strength that faith not only gives me, but the strength it has given others. I admire my mom, who has unwavering faith. Her childhood was not easy. She has lost many loved ones and tirelessly worked every day of her life. Through it all, she lit candles and asked for God's help to heal. I often wonder how she can continue to believe that God is real when her prayers have gone unanswered again and again. But when I discuss her faith, I can see throughout all her sadness and suffering, she remains strong. She doesn't blame God for not giving her the outcome she has requested. She instead thanks Him for standing by her through the suffering. God is not only her salvation for her afterlife. He is her salvation here on Earth.

I also think faith, religion, and church can give people a place to connect, to love, to belong. A church creates a community—people who not only pray together, but who work and play together—whether that involves a fish fry, bake sale, youth dances, or adult volleyball. Coming together to give time, talent, and treasure around a common cause isn't just good for a soul, it's good for a community.

❖ What do I hate about religion?

Although I often feel a sense of jealousy for those with unwavering faith and sometimes long for their certainty, I am often troubled by that same rigidity. I grow weary of those who cite scripture with such ferocity and staunchness that they seem unwilling to consider information that might run contrary to their prepared sermons. I also loathe that religion too often is an instrument to cast hate—for people with different faith, race, or sexual orientation. I am disturbed that religion selectively rejects science at times when it doesn't nicely fit into a narrative written thousands of years ago—whether that is views on the universe, evolution, or contraception.

For those who are not familiar with Catholicism, all the readings of Scripture and prayers for those attending the weekly church service, also called the Mass, are neatly organized into a prayer book called a missalette. My weekly attendance at church probably until about age thirty, along with my hour-long weekly religion classes from kindergarten through high school, formed most of my understanding of the Bible. I also have tried to dig into the Bible on my own, with the intention of reading it from cover to cover. But each time I started, my interest began to fade about the time that snake with legs hands a naked Eve an apple. So, suffice it to say, I am not a biblical scholar.

And yet, from my own readings and understanding of the text, I struggle to find it as the absolute infallible truth that should guide our spiritual awareness and our way of living. Although I find many of the stories in the Bible beautiful, I also find it puzzling why so many people fall back to this text as their sole source for believing and point me to the text as their evidence in an attempt to bring me certainty and salvation. I understand many believe this is the word of God, and God Himself is really the author, but surely they must wonder who actually put pen to paper (or reed to papyrus). Also, if one has based a belief about their way of life and their salvation prominently on this text and uses it to convince others of those same beliefs, isn't it critical to fully understand the historical origins of that text and to purposely seek out alternative texts that may provide opposing views? Furthermore, isn't it reasonably possible (and most likely plausible) that the people writing the text inaccurately reported or remembered all the events? And what is the likelihood that nothing has been lost in the hundreds of translations of that text?

Finally, even if everything written is as it happened, do all those stories appropriately guide us today? After all, to put the age of the text in context of how much has changed, it was less than two *hundred* (not thousand) years ago when no one in the world understood or believed in germs and it was legal to own another human being in the United States. If the thoughts of two hundred years ago seem inaccurate or misguided, surely we should remain a bit skeptical of texts from two *thousand* years ago. We would not use the Bible to guide our physical health, so why then do we view it as infallible to guide our spiritual beliefs or daily practices? Surely we have learned things over the last two thousand years that not only give us a more accurate truth, but make us better people.

I'm not suggesting everything in the Bible is flawed or false. I simply have trouble believing it is all true. Furthermore, I struggle accepting this text as the exclusive source on how to live a good life. After all, even my high school papers required me to cite at least three sources—even when I was just writing a paper about beagles.

Fewer books have spoken more directly to me than a book by my friend Phil Gulley called *Unlearning God: How Unbelieving Helped Me Believe*. Phil's book is amusing and uplifting but also pointed and challenging. He walks through his own life experiences with faith and religion with an approach that makes you laugh while simultaneously challenging deeply rooted beliefs. He pokes fun at his own religious exploration but drives home serious points by sinking his teeth into some common yet problematic views held by religious institutions. Phil takes on both the dogma and practices, squarely addressing delicate topics including sex, the role of women in church, the place for science in our faith, and much more. Chapter after chapter, Phil exposes what I see as the ugliness of religion, while also still shining a light on its beauty.

My own experience is that so much of what is taught by religions seems driven by fear. We are taught to fear the unknown, to believe that it is the devil that makes us question the words of the Bible, and to reject that which seems different, such as homosexuality. And yet, shouldn't real truth come from multiple sources—not just the Bible, but from science, and our own ability to use reason and logic? Shouldn't our thoughts be shaped by people with a wide range of perspectives—people who are believers and people who are non-believers? As Phil writes, "Truth is so robust, so vital, so immense, it could no more be contained in one book than the sun could be confined in a box. Religions can point to that truth, savor it, seek it, and celebrate it. But they can never grasp it in its entirety, or fully own it or control it."

Furthermore, I don't understand how one can label themselves a good, kind, accepting person who lives in the image of Christ, but then cast severe judgment on those who don't share the same beliefs. From a strictly historical perspective, the story of this man named Jesus seems to be about a person who viewed gratitude, fairness, acceptance, decency, tolerance, leadership, and service fundamentally differently than those around him. He did not create barriers or labels of those who were "in" and "out." There were not sides in his eyes. He not only washed the feet of his disciples, but he longed to be surrounded by both believers and non-believers—the righteous and the sinners. He wanted to spend time in villages with Samaritans, people who held different religious beliefs than his own, and befriended prostitutes. Every story I've read or been told about Jesus is about a man who loves and accepts others without condemnation.

Since my diagnosis with cancer, a number of good friends and well-intentioned people have sought to understand my faith and want to "save me." They want me to say with complete certainty that "I accept Jesus Christ as my Lord and Savior with all my heart and mind." I genuinely appreciate that others care so much about me that they are willing to give of themselves to help me. And yet I struggle to see how this belief system of needing to hold tightly defined beliefs of Jesus as the

Savior accurately reflects the life of the man to whom they want me to claim my allegiance. How can the story of the person who loved without boundaries or preconditions be the basis for why some will live an eternity in a fiery Hell, regardless of the life they have led? Surely not every Jew, Hindu, Muslim, or religious title that doesn't align to one church's teachings deserves an eternity in torture. Surely the people with a modified version of one person's truth or those with an inquisitive mind who question the teachings of the Bible or the interpretation of the Bible aren't also damned to the fiery hole.

When Anna Mae and Lizzie were toddlers, they asked me an endless list of questions. How far is the sun from Earth? Why do bees sting? If one giant stood on another giant, could the top one touch the moon? How do you make ice cream? What is war? Why are fireworks so loud? What causes cancer? What is death?

I'm sure every parent has experienced their own litany of questions from their children. They are constantly forming new questions, guessing answers, and testing whether their proposed answers align to the world that surrounds them. Everything is new—including discovering toes on their feet—and nothing is fully settled—including whether all ten toes can fit in their mouth at the same time. This natural insatiable curiosity is what I enjoy most about kids. But as they grow older, they are taught there are "right" and "wrong" answers and that there is such a thing as a dumb question or inappropriate actions, like putting your toes in your mouth.

I do want them to know the difference between knowing what actions are right and wrong, but I also want them to continue to search for the *truth*—on all topics. I miss their intellectual curiosity—their thirst to make sense of the world around them and bring meaning to the thoughts and emotions that stir within them. So, I want them endlessly searching for answers that can be explained through sound research, scientific methods, and reason. By doing so, who knows— maybe someday they will be able to answer the questions I wasn't able to answer for them. Perhaps it is their curiosity that will someday find the cause and a cure for cancer.

So, I struggle to accept that the secret to my own healing is believing in a god that can grant me that healing. I admire those in this world who didn't just attribute the disease and death of this world as God's will and had the courage and the resolve to search for scientific answers.

And yet, despite some of the ugliness that can come from religion and some uncertainty with my own faith, I want Anna Mae and Lizzie to see the beauty that comes from a relationship with God and a willingness to believe in something that may not be proven. After all, their faith may not help them understand what causes cancer, but perhaps it will be a source of strength and peace in managing the ugliness of the disease. And, believing in a higher power may not help them understand death, but it might make them become more accepting of it. And, by doing so, maybe they will "have faith" that, regardless of whether or not I am able to tuck them in at night, I will always be by their side.

CHAPTER 14:

WHO THE F*CK IS THAT?

Life Lesson: *Stay true to yourself even when everything around you is false.*

THE PROCEDURE TO REMOVE MY lymph node and look inside my abdomen went well. I came home with three marks in my abdomen signaling the place the scope had penetrated me, large Frankenstein stitches in my groin area where they removed a lymph node, and a new supply of pain meds I stubbornly refused to take because I hated the feeling of numbness. I wanted to ring out the last drips of *feeling* as much as I could.

I continued to go to work, go to my girls' games, do basic chores around the house, and cling to normalcy. But at night, lying in bed next to Tonya, my thoughts would be invaded like ants attacking an open container of sugar. I reflected on my life—on who I was in the past, who I had come to be, and who I wanted to become.

The last time I had thought deeply about my identity had been when I was in college. Although I went to Ball State University because of its strong architecture program, I was proud to learn that it was ranked as one of the nation's best party colleges while I was enrolled. I'm not suggesting it was given that title because of me, but since it had "earned" that reputation, I felt it was my responsibility to help do my part to keep that acclaimed designation intact.

Although I had my share of fun, I was a good student. In fact, according to my roommates whom I shared a house with my junior and senior year, I studied way too much. In truth, I did plenty of irresponsible stuff in high school so maybe I had met my quota for young adult stupidity as an adolescent. But I still found time to go to college parties and penny-draft nights. (Yes, penny-draft nights were a real thing. As in a really *bad* thing.) I was never the leader with my friends. So, especially as a freshman and sophomore, I was the goofy-looking guy with a dumb smile, carrying a plastic cup and following the crowd to the next house. My typical role was to cause plenty of laughs for the night but also be the one sensible enough to know when we better leave.

I liked to go to one particular house the most because a band I loved played in the basement. One of my college roommates we called Udo had introduced me to the house, some of the band members, and generally served as my guide both getting to the party and getting me home. The setup of the house was nearly like all the houses I had entered in the college town. They were modest homes, probably built in the 1950s or '60s. When you would enter the front door, you would step directly into a small living room and be greeted with a casual head nod from those in the room. The house with my favorite band usually didn't have a large mob of people in that first room. Instead, the living room consisted mostly of philosophy majors debating important topics like:

"At what point, if ever, does an old ship getting every board replaced become a new ship?" These students sat on dingy orange furniture that had begun to match the stained shaggy carpets. They were only partially visible with a cloud of smoke crushed up against the ceilings that smelled similar to when my parents raked and burned leaves at home.

Although I sat with this group a couple times, I usually didn't hang out there because I was committed to seeing the band in the basement—and, admittedly, I wasn't good at holding my own in the conversations since I didn't suck from the wisdom torch that got passed around. So, I would give my cool guy head nod, walk through the cloud of smoke and the small group of people, and make my way to the music. This involved going into the kitchen, taking a left, and then another left through the door, which led down a narrow, steep stairwell. I would enter my oasis that smelled like a mixture of mold and Busch Light and contained the energizing and mesmerizing sounds of R.E.M., Pearl Jam, Nirvana, Rush, and other legends—played by amateurs who I still viewed as rock stars. The basement was always packed with people. We would crowd together with just enough room to pound our heads to the music below the rafters.

I loved the music. I loved the energy. I loved the people. I loved the freedom. So, I started following Udo more frequently to my oasis. I even decided to go on my own one night when Udo couldn't make it, after doing some schoolwork in one of the campus computer labs. (My roommates were right; I did do a lot of homework.) Arriving at nine p.m. on a weekend was considered early, probably before the band had started, but I thought I would get a "front-row seat" (a square foot of concrete closer to the band).

I entered the house alone and saw a small group of only four or five people in the living room watching TV, without the clouds of smoke, the sounds of music, or debates I normally see. *So this is what it's like to be early*, I thought. I walked into the kitchen, took my usual left, and was ready to open the door to the steep stairwell, when I was apparently tossed into some weird new dimension. The door to the stairwell—no, the *entire stairway* wasn't there. I didn't see it vanish. But I know it was there last time and it was suddenly gone. Unexplainably gone! I looked around the kitchen. It also looked different. It definitely looked cleaner.

And, then, the conclusion hit me: I had just walked into a stranger's house.

I froze. It seemed like time itself stood still as I processed my situation: I had stormed through the front door of a complete stranger's house without knocking, gave my cool guy head nod and even added a "sup" for good measure, then proceeded into their kitchen, where I stood alone. I was considering my next move as I stood motionless in the kitchen, when the TV turned down slightly, and I heard a guy say to the others in the room with perfect clarity—even though he was trying to keep his voice low—"Who the f*ck is that?"

I looked back in the direction of where the stairwell should be. *Darn it! It's still not there.* I inspected the wall near where the stairwell should be for the back door that normally exists. It too was not there. So, without a better plan in place, I took a deep breath and walked back into the living room, gave another head nod, and walked out the front door without saying a word.

• • •

This happened more than twenty-five years ago, but I still think about the question pointedly posed that night. Although it wasn't particularly artfully asked, it was the question that needed to be asked. It's the question I have continued to ask myself most of my life: "Who the f*ck is that?"

In other words, who am I, really? Who was I then? Who am I now? If I had the courage and the thought, I would have popped back into the living room when cued with the question and said, "Hey guys. My name is Brad Fischer. I have a funny story to tell you." I would have hopefully gotten a good laugh and would have even invited them to my oasis to make up for my trouble. I still would have been the weird guy who walked into their kitchen, but who knows, maybe I'd even have made some new friends.

At that time, I was a guy still figuring out who I was, who my friends were, and who I wanted to be. I was struggling to decide whether to stay in the architecture program or to change my major to mathematics education. Although I had done well in the architecture classes, I couldn't see myself as an architect.

To be more specific, I couldn't see myself inside a French fry.

One of my projects in the freshman architecture studio program was to represent a word on a poster board and with a 3D model. The word I was assigned was *McPlace*. I really didn't know what they meant by the word, but I interpreted it as a word that represented the fast-food generation that had taken the creativity or guesswork out of the food industry. So, I was attempting to represent this by sketching some fries on my poster board when my brilliant and creative professor looked at it and said constructively, "I like the start, but I want you to picture yourself *inside* the fry. Look around. What is it you see? What do you smell? How do you feel? I want you to put that on the poster board."

As an adult, I actually like his advice. He was challenging me to not just look at things literally. He was inviting me to view the world more symbolically. French fries could represent more than an item in a McDonald's takeout order; they represented unhealthy eating habits, underpaid workers, big business, advances in food technology, and a hurried/rushed way of living. But as an eighteen-year-old freshman who loved numbers and found comfort in making predictions or even drawing clear answers by crunching through numbers, I literally had no idea what he meant. I knew how to solve for X. I didn't know how to step inside a fry. I simply thought my professor had spent too much time with the wisdom torch.

I was proud to call myself an architecture major for all the wrong reasons. Being an architect sounded impressive and important. I pictured myself with a pipe staring at a city skyline casually pointing out the buildings I designed. I applied to the program thinking I wouldn't get in, so when I was accepted, I felt like I was being invited to be part of an elite group. Most people knew the difficulty of being admitted to the program, which only fed my desire to let others know my major. In other words, I was pursuing a career because *others* were impressed by it.

I did well in the classes not because I cared about the material but because I cared about my grades. Although I now have admiration and appreciation for different styles of architecture, as an eighteen-year old, identifying buildings as Gothic, Renaissance, Baroque, or Rococo was like classifying my dad's collection of rotary telephones. They were all old. None of it interested me, and I certainly didn't care what it looked like inside a French fry.

Meanwhile, I was fascinated by learning about different mathematical infinite series and discovering that a sunflower followed the Fibonacci sequence. So, I knew—and had always known—that I really liked mathematics. I also wanted to share that love with others—especially people who hated math—so they too could experience its beauty. In short, I really wanted to be a math teacher. I just hated that being a teacher didn't impress others. I especially didn't want to disappoint my parents.

It was a difficult and unfamiliar time for me. Changing majors was scary. For the first time in my life, I felt like I was facing a decision that really mattered—that I thought would affect the rest of my life, that only I could make. And, I really had no idea what to do. Finally, I had the courage to ask my parents if they would be disappointed in me if I wasn't an architect.

Their response was simple and powerful: "Brad, we will be proud of you regardless. We just want you to be happy."

So, in the end, I chose to change my major to math education—not because it would impress others, but because it would serve others.

I taught math for only three and a half years. I really enjoyed it, but ended up gravitating to computers and have really centered on that work—supporting technology and doing data analytics for schools—ever since. If you would have told me when I was eighteen that I would be working for a technology company as an adult, I would have laughed incredulously. (I found computers intimidating most of high school.)

My point is that who we are changes. Our interests change. The friends we hang around will likely change. Opportunities change. The aspirations, skills, and mindset we have as freshmen in college will be different as a senior and certainly different when we are a middle-aged adult. And the only person anyone has to impress is themselves.

Embracing change is difficult, but necessary. It's how we learn. It's how we grow. When we have the courage to face our fears and accept new challenges, we don't just broaden our interests and our talents, we bolster our confidence in confronting new obstacles we face along the way. Selecting a major or career is not about picking a door to a room; it's about choosing a corridor that leads to more rooms. My advice to my daughters is to select a major and career that allows them to keep learning and growing. You want your choices today to give you more choices tomorrow because you never know what you'll be capable of accomplishing in the future.

I also want my daughters to be more focused on *who* they will be than *what* they will be. Currently, they are kind. They are thoughtful. They respect their bodies. They respect others. They are curious and creative. They are thankful. They are willing to work hard. These are the qualities that make me proud of them now and will continue to make me proud. But, more importantly, these are the qualities that will make them proud of themselves.

Sometimes I have the urge to start making a list of things I want them *not* to do. My prepared sermon goes something like:

- ❖ Don't do drugs.
- ❖ Don't drink alcohol until you are twenty-one (and then drink responsibly).
- ❖ Don't have sex until you are in a healthy, committed relationship and you are emotionally ready and prepared for possible consequences that follow, like becoming a parent.
- ❖ Don't play Shit Purse.

But, I know that my preaching isn't effective. Life is about learning from our own mistakes and being willing to accept the consequences of our choices.

I have not always made the best choices in life. I obviously broke a few rules in my journey. But thankfully my parents gave me that moral compass that always had me pointing in the right direction and the freedom to choose my own path. So when asked "Who the f*ck is that?" I can now say with pride, "I'm Brad Fischer. It's nice to meet you."

CHAPTER 15:

A BITE
IN THE BUTT

Life Lesson: It's a dog eat dog world, so don't be a dog.

As I WAITED ON THE biopsy results of the removed lymph node, I tried to keep my mind occupied. Because I was still feeling good, I was delighted to continue working each day—helping schools with their technology needs. I was thankful for my job and for the support from my bosses, colleagues, and clients. They were not just willing to stand with me, they were willing to carry me when I needed it. The work not only helped distract me during my treatments, it gave me a sense of purpose and a feeling of normalcy. Through all my treatments, I had brought my laptop, my loyal companion and diversion. I would keep my nose pointed at my screen and focused on emails, documents, managing software applications, and offering suggestions and advice to school administrators. Sitting in a chair in an infusion room while chemicals were pumping into my chest,

I would even occasionally participate in video calls trying to time my comments around the frequent beeps of the hospital monitors.

Not all my jobs throughout my life had been as personally rewarding. When I was in middle school and high school, I worked several odd jobs including baling hay, herding turkeys on a neighbor's farm, carrying out and stocking groceries at a local grocery store, and serving as a "mud boy"—the glamorous title given to the guy who mixed the mortar and carried bricks to the more skilled bricklayers on a construction job. Fortunately, during my senior year in high school, I ended up landing a great summer job at the local telephone company where my dad worked. I continued to work there most summers and school breaks until I graduated from college. My duties evolved with each summer, but included mail boy, painter, pea gravel hauler, weed eater, map man, phone support, and dispatcher.

Part of my job of updating maps was going house to house to see where telephone lines entered businesses and residences. I enjoyed the work—at least most days. One day I was in the backyard of someone's residence looking up trying to determine where the phone line entered their home. Without realizing it, I approached a doghouse while still staring into the air at the telephone lines. I was about ten feet from the doghouse when I heard the angry growl of what sounded like a dragon coming from inside the small wood enclosure.

The beast's head emerged, revealing it was a Rottweiler too big for its pen and that seemed to have an appetite for young men who draw maps. I froze, seeing the foam dripping from its mouth as it told me with a threatening growl to "back the @#&! up." So, I did. Slowly, very slowly, I started to back away from the doghouse. But that didn't please him either. He emerged from the house and growled at me some more. I continued to back up, keeping my eyes on his next move. But the farther I stepped away from him, the angrier he seemed to be getting—snapping his head forward, his growls becoming deeper and prolonged, flashing his teeth as if he was showing me that he was indeed part dragon.

He stayed in position as I continued to backpedal. I noticed he had a large chain hooked to a leash on his neck. I started some mental calculations: Could I escape the radius of his reach if I began to run? It was the classic math problem, the one where two trains leave a station at different times and you must calculate when they would meet. Although a good math problem typically would have caught my interest, my concentration was a bit rattled. And, besides, the dog–dragon didn't seem too interested in discussing the particular details of the situation—like the exact length of his chain or the speed at which he could run.

I wasn't sure if his next move was to breathe fire on me or to pounce on me and start chewing me to pieces. His angry growl changed to a deep throaty bark and he lunged forward. Even though I was ten or fifteen feet away from him, when he lunged, my flight instincts took hold and I began sprinting full speed away from the pen. As I ran, I could hear the chain unraveling and the sound of paws pounding on the ground chasing me. But just when I was sure I was going to be mauled, I heard the chain clang and the tug and whimper of my assailant being restrained. I looked back, saw the anger in his eyes, and continued to walk away with trembling legs as he continued with his loud scary barks, which—although I'm not fluent in dog language— certainly seemed to include unflattering comments about my mother.

As I retreated, I heard the higher-pitch barks of another dog. I looked over my shoulder and saw a second dog, who was also clearly agitated with my presence. Only, thankfully, this was a little dog—one that didn't even come to the height of my knees. It ran toward me but then stopped as I turned to study it. The little dog was filthy, looked malnourished, and overall angry with life. I felt a sense of sorrow for the dog but was also mostly relieved that it wasn't another Rottweiler on the prowl. So, I turned my gaze from it and continued to walk away.

Apparently the little coward saw its opportunity. It ran toward me, jumped up, and bit me right in the butt. I used my clipboard to swat the attacker away—but only after he was able to get two good chomps at my bottom, tearing through my jeans and my skin. I looked back at the Rott staring at me from the end of his chain. Despite his angry expression, I'm pretty sure he was laughing inside at what had just happened. In the end, I was thankful that it wasn't the fangs of the dog–dragon that pierced my cheeks, but my day still ended with a trip to the doctor's office for a few necessary shots.

Although I can't say I enjoyed that particular day of my job—or for that matter, my tenure as hay bailer, mud boy, or turkey escort—these experiences certainly taught me valuable lessons about work ethic, teamwork, and to expect the unexpected in any work environment. Since graduating from college, I feel fortunate to have jobs I've enjoyed and have been very lucky to find myself at the right place and time to move into better opportunities for myself and to serve others throughout my career.

I've also learned that whether hauling turkeys, mixing mortar, updating maps, teaching students, or directing technology projects, there are several things that all jobs have in common. I have identified four qualities that I think fundamentally cause us to take and stay in a job, which I call the four Ps of any profession:

❖ **Purpose** – Mark Twain said, "The two most important days in your life are the day you are born and the day you find out why." We shouldn't let our work completely define us, but we should define our work by finding purpose and pride in what we do.

My cancer diagnosis has caused me to think a lot about my own life and my purpose. When my time comes, whether that is four months from now or forty years from now, I hope others will look at my life and feel that I made a positive difference—that somehow, some way, I've left it a little better than when I entered it. It is the reason I became a teacher and continues to be the reason I find joy in my work—because I feel I'm doing something that matters.

Purpose in any job has less to do with *what* you are doing and everything to do with *why* you are doing it. Although a paycheck may help you fill your stomach, it doesn't fill your soul. Although I think the world would be better if we all sought ways to make it better in our jobs, that also doesn't mean we all must be doctors, first responders, or teachers. After all, I personally think there is meaning that comes from any job. Hauling turkeys is ultimately about putting food on the plate for others.

Mixing mortar is really about building homes for families. Updating maps for the phone company was ultimately about establishing accurate information for 911 calls.

Establishing purpose in a company isn't just good for others, it's good for business. Some of the most profitable companies became successful not because they were fixated on their profits, but because they were fixated on their purpose. As Steve Jobs, the late CEO and co-founder of Apple, one of today's most valuable companies in the world, once said: "Being the richest man in the cemetery doesn't matter to me. Going to bed at night saying we've done something wonderful, that's what matters to me." So whether you are a CEO of a wealthy company, a teacher, or mud boy, I challenge you to find how your job—your purpose—ultimately helps others and to show others in your organization the larger impact they are having.

❖ **Progress** – Not only do we want to feel like we're making a difference for others, most people want to feel they are learning and growing themselves in the process. We want to know that we contribute in a meaningful way to the team and that through hard work, persistence, and the support of others, we will continue to improve at what we are doing. This isn't about climbing the corporate ladder by pushing others off it. It is about extending a hand to others and feeling that each day the collective team is improving and getting a little closer to achieving their vision, their goals, their objectives. Progress is about becoming a better version of ourselves and about helping others do the same. It's about concrete short-term wins that keep a bounce in our step and about hard-fought, long-term victories that make us know all the effort was worth it.

❖ **People** – Unless you are being paid to paint ceramic unicorns alone in your basement, there is a good chance your job will involve working with other people. Those interactions—those relationships—often make all the difference in your satisfaction with a job and, if you're lucky, become relationships that last a lifetime. Like it or not, the reality is that most people end up spending equal or more time with colleagues than they do with their own family members, so it sure makes a difference if you work with people you respect and whose company you enjoy.

I have been fortunate to have worked with kind, thoughtful, talented people throughout my career. My various jobs and roles have allowed me to cross paths with students and adults of all ages and customers and clients who have put their trust in me. I've been surrounded by people who not only made my job better, but people who made *me* better—both professionally and personally. They have taught me about the importance of different personalities, perspectives, and strengths; the power of shared goals; the rewards of hard work; the value of patience and forgiveness; the healing of laughter; and the joy that comes from a job well done. I've had the privilege of serving others, working alongside others, and leading others. But whether I was leading or being led, I always felt like I was part of a team—a group of people who wanted to do something bigger than themselves.

❖ **Paycheck** – My dad used to tell me, "If it was supposed to be fun, they wouldn't call it work." Although I genuinely think work can be fun, I do think we sometimes do our children and ourselves a disservice by pretending work is supposed to *always* be fun. There also is a difference between fun and rewarding. And, certainly, there is a practical element that is a motivator for any job: our paycheck. Most of us take on at least our first job so we can live independently, which is something in itself that builds pride and confidence. Earning a paycheck teaches us the value of money and builds personal strength and character. I respect people earning an honest living regardless of their industry or their role—whether that involves hauling turkeys, mixing mortar, updating maps, teaching students, or running a company. The world needs all types of people and workers. And although I don't think money is the only—or even the most important—factor in a job, we should acknowledge that it remains a legitimate factor. A paycheck puts food on our table and is a concrete way we can feel valued for our effort and outcomes.

However, as we advance in our careers and our lives, money sometimes has a way of taking our eyes off why we wanted the paycheck in the first place. We may convince ourselves that a higher-paying job will make us happier because it provides more resources and more "stuff" for our family. However, the irony is that in an attempt to earn more money, we often end up adding stress, long hours, and more family friction that can ultimately have a way of eating away at the very happiness we think money will bring.

I hope my children are as fortunate as me to enter or create a career that not only helps put money in their pockets, but also puts happiness and satisfaction in their hearts. I hope they are able to surround themselves with genuinely good people and find both purpose and progress in their work. But I also want them to know that even the most rewarding jobs aren't always easy, fun, productive, or fulfilling. Sadly, not every colleague will be a great team player. Even kind, talented people who you respect dearly may frustrate you or disappoint you on given days. Likewise, you will make mistakes, have days where you aren't the best version of yourself, and certainly have times that you want to quit.

As lucky as I feel about my career and past experiences, I also admit that there have been moments in all my jobs where I unknowingly stumbled too close to the doghouse. As a mud boy, my boss yelled at me all day because he thought I had lost one of his tools—only to find it on the seat of his truck when we were leaving to go home. As a first-year teacher, I witnessed the anger of a parent whose child's grade had temporarily dipped from an A- to a B+ and endured the rage from the defiant student who refused to change seats. As a tech person early in my career, I was embarrassed, ashamed, and frustrated with myself after I accidentally deleted some important data that took days to recover. Either through faults of my own or actions of others, throughout my jobs and my career, I have had my share of moments when others have disappointed me or I've disappointed myself.

Even when you and all your colleagues are doing the very best you can, things can and will still go wrong. Every person, every team, every company has bad days. But sometimes it is the bad days that teach us the most—not only about others, but about ourselves.

And, yes, there will be times that despite feeling like you've made all the right choices and have given the job your all, someone or something will bite you in the butt. But like all disappointments in life, you will be judged not by whether or not some mangy mutt was able to sink its teeth into your bottom and bring you down. You will be judged by whether you had the courage and strength to push him away, brush yourself off, heal the wounds, move on, and ultimately help lift others up.

CHAPTER 16:

GET THE
FROG OUT

Life Lesson: Be willing to hop outside your comfort zone.

In addition to continuing to work, I felt good enough to go to the gym to work out. Even prior to my diagnosis, my exercise routine throughout my life had been pretty spotty. I had gone through several cycles of trying different workouts—lifting weights, running, and playing different sports. I typically was more motivated when there was a ball involved or others were chasing me. If I was running toward a goal, around bases, or charging a net, I seemed to focus less on the monotonous and tiring result of...well, moving.

Although I was a regular spectator at my girls' events, I didn't seem to have the same level of commitment when it came to my own activities. I had trouble committing to playing an organized sport multiple times a week, and, sadly, playing volleyball once a week didn't quite transform me into a chiseled Iron Man. So, a few years ago, after packing on a few pounds and finding myself waking up sore from simple activities like raking leaves, carrying boxes to the basement, or simply driving a car, I thought I might need to up my workout schedule.

Tonya had been saying how much she enjoyed her workouts at Hoosier Trainer, a local gym in Brownsburg, owned and led by a young woman named Monica. Tonya encouraged me to go with her to give it a try. So I did. I went to a RIPPED class. Since Tonya was attending, I was expecting other women to be there. What I wasn't expecting was *all* women. I walked into the gym and immediately felt like a duck out of water—a very green-headed mallard duck among the brown, black, and blond-headed ducks. I looked around the gym hoping to see another green head—more men—so I could more easily blend into the crowd. I finally spotted a guy in the back, but he also had a look on his face that made me think he had landed in this pond by mistake.

But I decided to man up and give it a shot. Following Tonya's directions, I grabbed a mat and set of barbells and tried to hide in the back the best I could. Monica turned on the music and started us with some leg stretches, quickly moving side to side. I followed along the best I could, mimicking Monica's moves. We went from stretches, to squats, bicep lunges, tricep kickbacks, lateral shoulder raises, and a host of other moves I was learning for the first time. And, although I had first thought that the weights I grabbed would be too light for me, I quickly realized that after the 150 reps we were doing, even the weight of my arms felt heavy. I was huffing and puffing and could feel my muscles aching, begging me to quit. I looked at the clock wondering if the fifty-minute workout was almost over, only to see that we were only ten minutes in.

As I struggled to keep up, I started to understand how this class got its name. I had originally thought RIPPED was given its name because it was a class that would give me greater muscle definition. You know, it would make me ripped. I then read that RIPPED was really an acronym for resistance, interval, power, plyometrics, endurance, and diet. But as I struggled through a set of burpees trying to catch my breath, I realized that it was more likely an abbreviation for all those who died trying this insane workout. They were RIPed alright, as in resting in peace.

But I managed to keep going. Each time I thought I was about to crack, Monica would shout with encouragement that we just had a couple more. So, I would convince myself to do another couple more. And when I was sure I was done, she would switch to something else. So, when I was ready to die from burpees, we would move to side kicks. And right when I was ready to call it quits on side kicks, she would transition to something else, like mountain climbers.

It wasn't only Monica's encouragement that kept me moving; it was the commitment of all the others in the class. Sure, a part of me didn't want to be embarrassed for quitting, but it was more than that. I felt like if others could do it, surely I could too. And, finally, even though my muscles were in agony, the reps went to the rhythm and counts of the upbeat music. There were brief moments when we were all shuffling left and right to the music that I thought we must look like a bad MC Hammer music video. Even though my body felt like an old man, my brain felt like a teenager on a dance floor wanting to keep jamming to the music.

So, by the end, my T-shirt was wet with sweat. My arms quivered when I returned the mat and my legs wobbled stepping off the sidewalk into the parking lot. I felt completely exhausted. Although I was out of step a good portion of the time, some women used heavier weights than me and made it look easy—and although I was forced to skip some reps to take a few extra breaths, I felt proud and accomplished that I had completed the class without quitting or dying.

Even though I woke up sore the next day, after a few days passed, I did find myself hoping to go back. Our family schedule made it difficult for Tonya and me to go at the same time. The girls needed one of us to shuttle them to their activities, so we decided to alternate our schedules, with Tonya going some evenings and me going others. I was glad to be returning, but I also felt even more uncomfortable showing up without Tonya. I wanted to wear a T-shirt that said, *I'm not a creeper. I just like the workout.*

Nonetheless, I showed up alone. I kept my head down and made my way to the back of the room trying to be as stealth-like as possible. In the workout space, there is a large side garage door that Monica will leave open on nice weather days. It was raining outside, but the cool breeze felt refreshing. I stood with my mat and weights quietly in the back ready for the music to begin. But right as the music began and Monica started counting our first set of squats, a young lady came up to me from behind and flatly said, "Excuse me. Could you get the f— out?"

I wasn't certain the F word she used rhymed with "duck." However, I was pretty sure the message was the same: she was wanting me to leave. A mixture of embarrassment and resentment began to flood my brain. Maybe I should have worn the *not a creeper* T-shirt. Or, maybe this workout truly was exclusive for women. Maybe it was no different than me stepping into the wrong restroom. I turned and looked at her expression. She was smiling. I was relieved, but puzzled. My resentment and embarrassment were replaced by confusion. "Excuse me?" I finally muttered, hoping I did not understand her correctly.

"Can you get the frog out?" she repeated more clearly with the smile still on her face.

Although I didn't have time to search the expression on my phone, I assumed "get the frog out" was equal to "get the flip out"—a slightly softer and more playful way of asking me to exit. I stood there completely confused with how to respond. Surely she must be joking. She clearly was not angry with me, but why was she asking me to leave? So, I smiled and repeated the question. "You want me to get the frog out?"

"Yes," she said with a smile again, but this time she pointed to the floor along the back wall.

Surprisingly—and delightfully—I witnessed a small frog hopping around in the back of the room. He wasn't particularly good at keeping rhythm to the music and wasn't even trying to follow Monica's lead with the leg squats.

"Sure," I said, feeling like a fireman ready to storm a fiery building (even though the task was more like retrieving a small kitten from a tree). I briskly approached the frog, ready to confront his shenanigans. His random bouncing from side to side stopped and he froze along the wall, pretending to be decoration. As I bent down to grab him, he took a giant leap forward, escaping my grasp. He hopped right and back left, I followed him, bent down, and scooped him up with my hands.

I wanted to give him a pep talk before I set him free, but I also was still trying not to be the weird guy. So, I walked out of the garage door and without much fanfare set him on the ground and watched him rapidly hop away thinking, *Sorry little guy. It was either you or me that had to go.*

Most didn't even notice all this activity unfolding in the back of the gym, but as I walked back into the gym, a couple of the ladies quietly clapped. The young lady who had brought the frog to my attention added in an affirming voice, "Thanks. You looked like someone who could handle a frog."

My chest swelled with pride as if I had slayed a dragon to protect Monica's kingdom and all her loyal people. I still felt a little uncomfortable being the only guy in a gym full of women. My timing and rhythm in the workouts definitely needed some work. And, I certainly had a long way to go to get in as good of shape as the others in the class. But I was someone who could redirect an adrift amphibian. I was the guy who could catch a frog! I had faced my admission test and passed.

And so, I continued my workouts at Hoosier Trainer. I didn't always get to go as frequently as I liked, but I managed to go a couple times a week and always felt better after going. I also felt less like an odd duck in a strange pond. In addition to seeing a few more guys join the club, Brenda, the kind receptionist, would greet me at the door with a big smile and warm welcoming "hello" and "so glad to see you"—making me feel like part of a family.

After my cancer diagnosis, I wondered if I would go back. After starting chemo, I felt so terrible that my "workout" consisted of me walking to my kitchen from my bedroom. I wondered if it was the beginning of my end. I wondered if my health would continue to deteriorate and when I would not have the strength to continue. What I found surprising is how much I missed Monica's classes—not just the physical benefits that it gave me, but the emotional and mental boost I would feel each time I went.

So, even as I was continuing my rounds of chemo, I started going again. The neuropathy in my hands and feet made it harder. The pressure and twinges in my stomach would make me pause at times, but pushing through it seemed to help me accept the discomfort. I tired more quickly than before, but it still had a way of energizing me the next day. It became therapy for me—a way for me to feel alive, a way to struggle, but heal. It wasn't a way to mask the pain, but a way to lean into discomfort and to fully feel it.

What I have learned is that my workouts are no longer about others. After my diagnosis, I started worrying less about what others may be thinking. Being embarrassed for being out of rhythm, out of step, or the green-headed mallard suddenly seemed insignificant. I wasn't there to impress anyone. I no longer focused on what I should look like or be able to do in a workout. I was there for me. I wanted to become a better version of myself. And, I certainly still had plenty of room for improvement—not just in my physical health but in all my personal qualities.

The same is true for others working on their own self-improvement—whether that is to become healthier physically, mentally, or emotionally. We need to move away from comparison and be a better workout buddy to ourselves. Not only do we bring our individual, special body type into a room, we each bring our own unique experiences, challenges, and yes, suffering. Whether we are fit or flabby, old or young, tall or short, male or female, or have lived an easy life or difficult life, we too often try to fit in and compare ourselves to others even though their life story is often completely different than our own. Instead, we should take a moment each day to celebrate what makes each person unique and strive to be a better version of ourselves.

Our uniqueness doesn't make us the *exception to* a group; it makes us *exceptional in* a group. And when it comes to working out—and life in general—the measure that matters most isn't our waistline, the size of our biceps, or the baggage we bring into a room. What matters most is our tenacity to struggle and sweat, our eagerness to root each other on to do one more rep, our joy from dancing with others, our strength to let go of our fears and insecurities, and our courage to confront the obstacles in our lives and our fortitude to—when necessary—get the frog out!

CHAPTER 17:

TIME-OUT

Life Lesson: In the game of life, play hard, take water breaks, and have a ball.

THE SCORE WAS 45 TO 43 as my players hustled back on defense to defend their two-point lead. I stood on the sideline switching my attention from the score clock back to my team, a group of eighth-grade boys at Danville Community Middle School, who were now playing man-to-man defense against one of our county rivals, Avon Middle School. With sixteen seconds to go, the whistle blew and the official signaled a shooting foul against us. Before the referee handed the kid the ball for two attempts from the free-throw line, I signaled a time-out. I wanted to talk with my players and make him think about his shots.

My players hustled over to the bench. Their energy and nervousness poured out of them as they huddled around me to hear my words of wisdom. I immediately quieted down their nervous chatter and asked them to focus. I explained the strategy as carefully as possible.

"Be sure to block out on the shots to get the rebound." I stared into their faces dripping with sweat, making sure I had their attention, then added, "If he hits both free throws, take the ball out of bounds, get it in and push the ball across half court just like we've practiced this week. After you get the ball past half court, call time-out." I paused for a moment, looked again at the players, then extended my fist for our ritual chant. As the hands stacked on top of my fist, I said with a fierceness in my voice, "Let's finish this!" then counted down, "Three, two, one..."

The team screamed in unison "Warriors!"—which was our team mascot, but more importantly, our battle cry.

I watched the players find their place around the free-throw line. The referee handed the boy the ball. He took a few dribbles and shot. The ball landed softly over the front of the rim, vibrated for a moment around the rim then fell through the net. The opposing fans howled, seeing their deficit cut to only one point. The kid stepped back up to the line, received the ball, dribbled a few times, shot. Nothing but net. Tie game.

Our players grabbed the ball, scurried out of bounds, and tossed it in as instructed. The other team remained in their full-court press. After a few passes we managed to get the ball across half court. The Avon players rotated their defense and our guard found himself trapped just across the half-court line. The clock showed ten seconds.

I started shouting as loud as possible to my players, "Time-out! Time-out! Time-out!" The noise of the gym drained out my voice. The boy being trapped managed to get around one defender and passed it to one of our players standing in the center of the court—barely on our side of the line. "Time-out! Time-out! Time-out!" I screamed again.

The clock ticked down: 5, 4, 3, 2… And at the very last moment, one of our players hurled the ball from half court toward the goal. The ball arched through the air in complete silence—as if it was a particle floating peacefully in space—with everyone in the gym following its gravitational pull to the rim. The ball buried itself into the bottom of the net and a roar of cheers filled the gymnasium. The Danville student fans began charging onto the court with exhilaration and to embrace the hero who made the half-court shot.

I stood watching the celebration begin to unfold. Before I let my emotions shift into celebration, I looked back at the referee. He stood at half court, waving his arms repeatedly outward with his whistle in his mouth, which I now heard, but only barely above the roar of the crowd. He was waving the shot off—signaling it did not count.

Bewilderment and anger gushed into every ounce of my body. The shot was clearly released before the horn signaling the end of the game. How in the world could he be waving off the shot?! I paced toward him. But before I even got to him, his waving arms stopped for a moment—with only one hand in the air and the other pointed squarely at our bench. And as I got only a few feet from him, I heard him flatly repeating, "Time-out, Red."

Apparently, as one of our players was dribbling to escape his defenders, one of our other players had finally caught the attention of the referee signaling a time-out—just as I had requested on the bench, just as I had been screaming. In the commotion and noise, no one heard his whistle, including the person running the clock. But he insisted that he had been signaling the time-out with two seconds remaining. The shot did not count. It didn't count because some stupid coach—me—called a time-out right before the shot.

It took a few minutes to clear the court and get all the fans settled back into the bleachers. Our players came to the sideline deflated. I tried to feign confidence. I put out the small whiteboard, called out our inbound play, and drew it out again—trying to make sure we were focused on the next shot, rather than the shot that had just been erased from the scoreboard. The team left the huddle again after our ritual chant. On the sound of the whistle, our team executed the play perfectly. One of our players, wide-open and about ten feet from the goal, released the ball just before the buzzer. The ball struck the front of the rim and spun forward, rolled around the rim. And dropped out.

The game went to overtime. We ended up losing.

I relived that play for several days after that game. I was playfully harassed by the varsity coaches who found joy not only in the story, but in seeing my misery of recounting the play. Being a relatively new coach, I genuinely sought the advice of the more seasoned coaches. Should I have instructed the players to take it to the goal from the beginning? Was a time-out the right strategy? There really wasn't consensus on the strategy itself. I was informed that even among a room full of talented, seasoned coaches, about half would approach it the way I did. With fifteen or more seconds left, many liked the idea of getting the ball across half court but then calling a time-out for a set play for a better shot. Other coaches thought it would be better to push the ball to the goal for a shot without the time-out, in hopes of catching the defense more by surprise.

I took solace in knowing my approach at least had its merit. I also tried to convince myself that we had a much higher percentage shot after the time-out. But regardless of what I told myself, there was no denying one simple truth: my time-out cost us the game.

Play on or take a time-out? That is also the question I have often asked myself about the circumstances and situations I have faced in life. On many things, I tend to be a planner. For example, when I buy a car, I have to read *Consumer Reports*, test drive at least three cars, and read reviews and other facts online. I can drag out the process literally for months. But I also love being flexible, adaptable, and spontaneous at times—reacting to the moments that life presents me. Some of my best memories of trips have been when we didn't have a hotel or itinerary planned. We had a rough idea of what we wanted to accomplish and let each moment drive the next decision—even if that meant we got lost on a hike in Bali or stranded on an island in Thailand (both of which happened).

Sometimes the hardest thing to do is to wait and do nothing.

I continued to wait for the pathology report from my lymph node and other tissue samples. I waited wondering if the cancer was continuing to chew through my body. I waited to be told whether there was nothing more they could do or that the immunotherapy appeared to be working, whether it made sense to continue with my treatment. I waited to find out if I was another patient at the mercy of the spread of an unstoppable metastatic gastric cancer or whether I was a beneficiary of the latest advances in cancer research and treatment. I waited. Two days turned into seven days. And I waited.

As I waited, I found peace in remembering that by definition a time-out—waiting—means I still have time. After all, no time-out in basketball or any other sport has ever been called after the final buzzer sounded. I decided I may not know the news I will be given tomorrow, but I know the gifts I had been given that day. I knew that despite having surgery, I woke up feeling strong. I was able to take a shower, go to work, help my kids with homework, take Anna Mae to a friend's house, watch Lizzie's soccer game, empty and load the dishwasher, enjoy a cup of coffee, watch the beauty of snow and ice cling to the trees outside, and spend some time writing. Perhaps not knowing was better than knowing a fate that I wasn't ready to accept.

While waiting, I also recognized that I'm not alone in the juggling act of "playing on" and "taking a time-out" in the events that fill our lives. I watched Lizzie play on in her soccer game—using her competitive spirit and courage not to back down from the opposing team that had a girl nearly twice her size. I also watched her enjoy a time-out, talking and laughing with friends at lunch. I watched Anna Mae play on by going to a friend's house to help her organize her room. I watched her take a time-out to still give me a hug when she came back home. I watched Tonya play on by managing to direct the family through the commotion of each day—somehow putting her own emotions to the side—so we all could get to the places we needed to be. But I also saw her take a time-out by warmly grabbing my hand when I joined her under the covers at night. Ultimately, life remained a balance between playing on—taking action, facing my fears, doing the best I could—and time-outs—reflecting on the day, being grateful for my blessings, and soaking in the joy of each moment.

In basketball, you are not allowed to call a time-out when you are on defense. Regardless of which opposing player has the ball and regardless of what play the team is running, you must defend it the best you can. The same is true in life. Sometimes you must have the courage and strength to play on. As I continued to defend this terrible disease that was a relentless opponent, I braced myself for whatever news I would be given. I had to find my footing and face it head on. I took comfort in knowing when I stumbled at times, my teammates—my family and friends—would slide over to help. And because of that coverage, because of that support from all my fans, I continued to smile and enjoy each moment of the game.

SECTION 3

LOVE

"How lucky am I to have something
that makes saying goodbye so hard."

– WINNIE THE POOH

LOVE IS THE MOST POWERFUL force that brings meaning to my life. We know it when we see it, and we know it when we are spreading it or failing to spread it. But, most of all, we know it when we feel it. Love can sometimes best be expressed by a welcoming touch: from a big bear hug extended to family and friends to the gentlest pat on the back from doctor to patient. It can evoke intense feelings and comfort our nerves. It is both that simple and that complicated.

I want to…

❖ Be present for my family and friends. Not just show up for events, but be mentally and emotionally present.

❖ Be more sensitive to others' suffering and to let them know that I'm sorry they have to go through their struggles and that I am here for them.

❖ Fight for and contribute to causes that will make this world a better place now and for generations to come.

Examples of things that make me feel love...

- ❖ Receiving all the comments, prayers, and cards since my diagnosis.
- ❖ Witnessing simple acts of kindness, such as a hug, a note, a pat on the back, a kind word to someone who needs it most.
- ❖ Seeing people have the courage to do what is right even when it is extraordinarily difficult.
- ❖ Tucking my girls into bed at night.
- ❖ Having Tonya grab my hand after I crawl into bed.

CHAPTER 18:

SKATING THROUGH LIFE TOGETHER

Life Lesson: Fall in love. If you choose correctly, you will like where you land.

I MET TONYA, THE PERSON who would become my soulmate, my best friend, my wife, the mother of my children, about the same time that it was announced I was gay.

Let me explain.

I graduated from college in December and was stepping into my first teaching job in January at Roosevelt Middle School in Monticello, Indiana. I taught seventh-grade math. Tonya taught seventh-grade language arts in the classroom adjacent to mine. Tonya and I, along with other teachers, met over the Christmas break. She was dressed in black from head-to-toe: black sheath dress, black tights, and black lace-up Dr. Martens. After that first encounter, if you would have asked me to describe her, I would have said she's pleasant, short, a fan of coffee, a little artsy, a little overwhelmed, tired, and definitely *alternative*. In the early 1990s, "alternative" was the label used to describe people who didn't dress or behave in a way that aligned with the mainstream. It was also the word that had become a musical genre a few years earlier for bands that were emerging from the underground, like Pearl Jam, Nirvana, and The Smashing Pumpkins. Although I loved alternative music, the alternative look—especially mixed with lots of black—was a little freaky to me. So although I did find something attractive about her, let's just say I didn't see this person as the mother of my future children.

The first week of teaching was tough for me. I had pictured my students sitting on the edge of their chairs waiting to hear my brilliant ideas about math and laughing at my subtle, dry-witted jokes. Instead, they really didn't seem all that interested in any of my ideas about math and—even worse—didn't think I was particularly funny. But I was confident I could win them over.

There was a roller-skating party at the end of school on Friday most of the students would be attending. Chaperoning this might be a good way to connect with the students and a helpful start to build that necessary positive rapport. Right as we were ready to head to the roller-skating rink, one of my friends from college, Tommy, stopped by the school to see how I was doing and to see if we could celebrate surviving a week of teaching with a few drinks. Since that wasn't an option at that moment, I invited him to join us at the roller-skating rink so we could catch up there and grab drinks afterward. He decided to join us. We talked at the roller-skating rink. We even both skated. The students seemed to have fun and so did we. Everything went well. Until Monday morning.

On Monday morning, my assigned teacher mentor, Candice, asked to talk with me. She asked me how the skating went. I told her it was fun and talked about some of the activities. She asked if a friend of mine came with me. I said he did and started to apologize if he was supposed to pay for his skates. "It's okay he didn't pay," she interrupted. "I just want to let you know what the students are saying this morning. They said Mr. Fischer brought his boyfriend roller skating with him and they were skating holding hands together."

I was speechless. I had spent my college preparation learning instructional strategies, curriculum, higher level mathematics, and psychology. But never in all that training was I taught how to "in" myself. At the time, I'm ashamed to admit, I also was homophobic and too insecure to accept a label that was inaccurate, but also irrelevant, to my effectiveness. So, after sitting in disbelief for a moment, I said, "We weren't holding hands, and I'm not gay." Trying to add proof, I shared that Tommy was married with a kid. Candice listened and was understanding and supportive of me being a heterosexual.

But I left her room thinking, *What do I do with this information?* How was I to address a very personal, delicate topic with a room full of seventh graders I barely knew? Would I start each period saying something like, "Today we are studying how to add fractions by finding common denominators. And, speaking of that, the guy who was at the roller-skating rink and I have a lot in common, but we are not combining like terms, if you know what I mean. Uh, what I mean is you know how we talked about different geometric shapes the other day? Well, I find concave and convex polygons pair better together. Not that two concave shapes couldn't get along or go together... Or convex shapes for that matter... And, not that anything is wrong with that... But, I personally get uncomfortable when two convex shapes are overlapping... Now that I mention that...I also get uncomfortable picturing some convex and concave shapes overlapping... And, after all, if the shapes seem happy, why should I care? My point, though, is I like concave shapes. Some of you may still be figuring out your own geometric orientation. That's okay. I am here to support you either way. And, by support, I mean please talk to your parents about it, not me. But if you need help adding your fractions, I'm your guy. Are there any questions?"

Instead of confronting my own homophobia or the misguided positions of others, I shamefully fretted about how to remove the inaccurate label from myself. I also had no idea how to talk about one's sexual orientation and hated the elephant in the room stomping on all my lessons. I started the first period without a game plan. As the students came into the room, I greeted them and found myself wondering if I was emitting gaydar at that moment. Before the bell rang, there was the common chatter among the students and I thought maybe it was best to leave it unaddressed, until a girl who was gathered around her friends asked above the morning chatter, "Mr. Fischer, do you have a girlfriend?"

In an instant, the entire room grew silent and all eyes focused on me.

So, I took a deep breath and said, "No, I don't. But thanks for asking because it came to my attention that a rumor has been spreading." And I proceeded to explain how the rumor wasn't true and spoke about the damage that rumors can cause—not just this one but others. I asked how many of them ever had something that others shared about them that wasn't true? All the hands went up. And, as the conversation unfolded, for the first time, I found the students warming to me, trusting me, respecting me. They still didn't share my love for math. They still didn't think I was funny. Some probably still thought I was gay. But most genuinely seemed to appreciate that I was honest and vulnerable with them, that I was there to support them, and that I needed their help not just with this situation, but with anything we might tackle in the classroom. I quickly learned that teaching a lesson in geometry had very little to do with understanding the properties of shapes and everything to do with understanding the perspectives of people.

As the year progressed, I also spent more time with Tonya. Even after this incident, I continued to struggle with first-year teacher issues. Tonya became a supportive ear and someone willing to admit that she was facing her own challenges. (And, BTW, for any students I had those first few years of my teaching career, I'm sorry. I hope I didn't screw you up too badly.) I didn't see Tonya as this frightening alternative teacher, but as someone with a big heart and warm smile.

We started taking classes at Purdue that following summer, spending a lot of time together. In one of our classes, a classmate was arguing that spreading inappropriate or inaccurate information online (or on the "World Wide Web" as we called it) was equivalent to posting false or inappropriate information on physical signs. I pictured someone hammering signs on a telephone pole and scurrying to the next pole. The lady seemed determined to make that case until she unexpectedly paused, changed her expression as if she had an epiphany, then amended her point adding, "It just might take a lot longer." Her passionate argument abruptly followed by her concession struck my funny bone.

I didn't want to be rude, yet laughter began to swell inside me. Fearing my internal laughter valve would burst, I turned away hoping to gain composure. Instead, I witnessed Tonya shaking with laughter desperately trying to avert her eyes from the woman's emphatic look.

In the end, it still ended up being an awkward moment, with only the two of us laughing—feeling ashamed and guilty for finding any of it funny. But that was the moment I realized Tonya was someone who shared my warped sense of humor and was clearly someone I needed to spend more time with.

So, I started grilling chicken breasts on a portable propane grill outside my apartment and invited her for dinner and to watch the Indiana Pacers. We would talk about school, politics, religion, and watch "character-driven" movies I thought were boring. And, as we did, I learned that she was incredibly smart, cared deeply about creating a better world for others, and had a range of interests way wider than mine. She didn't just bring me laughter and joy and comfort and support when I needed it, she disagreed with me, challenged me, and convinced me to see a more diverse, complicated, beautiful world.

My physical attraction for her grew, much sooner than her to me. But eventually my charm—or chickens—began to win her over, because we became more than friends. Although I will never forget our first kiss, I'll leave those details out of this story. For me, and her, I don't think the attraction was binary, where it was off and then on. Instead, I felt like an electromagnet with someone steadily increasing the amps to pull me closer. The more time I spent with her, the more

I wanted to be with her. At first, I questioned whether the force would last. I thought perhaps the attraction was out of convenience. We were two young teachers who needed each other. I even made the decision to move away from her to take a job back in my hometown because she didn't seem as drawn to me as I was to her. But the force kept increasing. And over time, I found it to be absolutely irresistible.

After dating for several years, I proposed to her using a puzzle that I had made with photos of us that read, *Buddy, you fit me. Will you marry me?* She said yes. And so, after some planning, on July 20, 2002, we woke up early on the Big Island of Hawaii, took a difficult trek across some lava rock, and dove into a tide pool to go snorkeling. Whether life was rough and hard to navigate like the lava rock or as refreshing and peaceful as the tide pool, I knew I wanted to spend the rest of my life with this person. Later that afternoon we got married.

I often think about our relationship from an outside perspective and giggle thinking about that "gay math teacher" and "alternative language arts teacher" getting hitched. I'm sure we didn't seem like a likely couple. And yet, nothing I've ever done ever felt so natural. We've been blessed to have spent our marriage soaking in the sunshine inside the tide pool enjoying the beauty surrounding us. But even as I faced the battle for my life against cancer, stumbling on sharp, ragged lava rocks trying to move forward, there was no one else I wanted more by my side on the journey than Tonya.

I don't claim to be an expert on love or relationships. But I think the healthiest relationships are ones that just seem to fit. Since I considered using geometric shapes to explain my sexual orientation to my students, it feels only fitting to share my view of love using the same analogy. When Tonya and I met, I was an equilateral triangle. I was a simple—yet steady and reliable—building block. Tonya was a hexagon, a shape with considerably more sides or perspectives in how she viewed the world. She made me a better person by bringing out a zest for travel, appreciation of different cultures, and broadening of interests. I would like to think I made her better by being a practical voice of reason, source of laughter, and force for staying calm and focusing on the good during difficult situations. We didn't just become the sum of our parts, forming a nine-sided polygon. Our relationship feels more like a tessellation, like the image below, where an unexpected but beautiful pattern emerges.

We didn't have to work hard at forming our tessellation. It began to emerge, naturally, organically. Certainly we have experienced forces—like having kids, taking on new financial obligations, and facing new life challenges—that cause our shape to bend and warp a bit. But even during those times, we know that we are a team; we are a tessellation. We are no longer just a triangle and a hexagon.

So, to my daughters and future grandkids, and really anyone who may one day be seeking a committed relationship, I offer these questions:

❖ Does the person make you happy? Does the person make you smile, make you laugh, make you feel joy when you are together?

❖ Does the person make you a better person? Does the person stretch your interests or complement your weaknesses? Do they make you a more thoughtful, kinder, fuller person?

❖ Do you trust and respect the person? Is the person reliable, trustworthy, committed, and willing to work hard?

❖ Is this the person you want by your side during the best of times and worst of times? Life will certainly continue to bring you surprises. Is this the person you want with you during that journey?

❖ Does this person "fit" you? Are you able to be yourself when you are with the person and do you connect with each other easily, naturally, almost effortlessly?

If the answer is "yes" to all five, you may have a keeper. But if the answer is "no" to any of these questions, this may not be the person for you. Life is too short and too difficult on its own to feel like you are carrying the burden of a bad relationship through that journey. When you do find that person who's right for you, which I hope you do, lace up your roller skates, hold hands as tightly as possible, be ready and willing to help each other up when you fall, but most of all, smile, laugh, and enjoy the ride.

CHAPTER 19:

FLOATING AWAY

Life Lesson: *Dive with a buddy by your side. Live that way too.*

SHORTLY AFTER WE WERE MARRIED, Tonya and I decided to pick up a new hobby and become scuba certified. On our first wedding anniversary, we decided to put our skills to the test by going diving in Cozumel, Mexico. I awoke early the morning after our arrival and was eager to see our surroundings. Like a small child, I scurried down the steps outside our door and headed toward the whooshing sound of the waves on the shore. The view seemed surreal. The teal water reflecting the vibrant sunlight extended as far as my eye could see. Although I had been to the Caribbean Sea previously and other oceans a number of times, I gazed at its magnificence as if viewing it again for the first time.

My interactions with the "deep blue" up to this point had largely been that of a spectator, but this visit was certainly different. This time I would be a small particle in its incredible vastness, viewing the seafloor and fish that lie hidden below. Seeing a large boat rise and curl into the dock that held its ropes, I paid deference to the force I would soon enter. My anxiety also started to build. Images of running out of air, becoming lost at sea, or being surrounded by a swarm of jellyfish filled my head.

My next stop was the dive shop, where a young man with a jovial smile and warm, welcoming dark-brown eyes appeared from the back room. "*Hola, señor!*" the man said, approaching the counter.

"*Hola*," I replied, trying to reciprocate the language spoken. Sadly, however, with that one word, I had exhausted nearly all the Spanish I knew.

"How can I help you?" he politely asked in English, obviously decoding from my single "*Hola*" that I was one of those tourists who hadn't learned to speak Spanish. He pointed to a nearby clipboard with a list of names and added, "Are you signed up to go diving?"

I explained that Tonya and I were beginning divers and that we might sit out from the boat trips that day to build our experience and comfort level with a few shore dives, but I was interested in the week's dive schedules. Using my father's knack for making small talk with strangers, I found myself talking to him as if he had been an old friend. I learned that his name was José and that he had been a divemaster at the resort for the last five years, running the dive shop and serving as the dive guide for groups regularly. Our conversation stopped momentarily when another worker entered the small shop, grabbing his attention. The two guys had a brief conversation in Spanish and José faced me again with a smile.

José boasted, "There is a boat available this evening for a short time. If you like, I can take you and your wife out on a personal dive to make you feel more comfortable." He paused then added, "At no fee." The opportunity seemed as good as it could get: our own personal divemaster on our own personal boat for no fee. After discussing it with Tonya, we thankfully accepted his offer.

Tonya and I practiced our dive skills with a few shore dives that morning and afternoon. While waiting for the boat that evening, José briefly explained the plan for the dive. "We will take a boat out that is dropping off other people. We'll have the driver take us out to that first buoy," he said, pointing outward to the sea toward a marker that bobbed in the waves and added, "We'll descend and ride the current to a second buoy about five hundred meters from the first one. Then we'll start swimming across the current to our beach."

Tonya and I exchanged nervous glances. I gulped and then reiterated our situation. "We really want to start with something basic and don't want to go deeper than thirty feet."

"You'll have no problem," he said assuredly. Pointing at the small white vessel nearing the shore, he added, "Here comes our boat. Get your gear ready."

We walked away toward the lockers both questioning the sanity of this new hobby. Tonya spoke first. "What do you think about this?" she asked with a break in her voice.

Feigning confidence, I replied, "Let's go for it."

I tried to rationalize the situation to ease my fears that boiled inside. We'll have our own personal divemaster. The skies were clear and the sea looked relatively calm. We had completed shore dives that morning without any major obstacles. This was our moment.

The boat arrived and pulled up next to the dock. We clumsily made the transfer from the dock to the boat with José transferring our tanks and scuba gear. After we were seated, the driver of the boat pulled away from the dock and navigated toward the first buoy marker, a small shimmer in front of a backdrop that was nothing but a line dividing sky and water. As we increased our distance from the shore, Tonya and I hastily tried to get ready. We zipped up our wetsuits, attached the air tanks to our vests—or BCDs, as they are called—put on our masks and fins, and began testing our regulators.

We both felt a bit disheveled trying to get into our gear as we rocked in the small boat fighting across the waves. We arrived at the first buoy and the boat engines began to quiet. The sun was nearing the horizon and I could tell José was trying to hurry us along. As we fumbled with our gear, José sat on the edge of the boat, looked at us, then muttered, "I'll meet you down at the bottom." And then he stuck his regulator in his mouth, held his hand over his mask, and in a swift motion rolled backward off the boat.

I was shocked. I expected a pep talk, someone to double-check my gear, a ten- or fifteen-minute review, and frankly a lot of hand-holding on this first dive. But just like that, José was gone with bubbles coming to the surface serving as the only sign of his existence. Tonya and I stared blankly at each other sitting on the boat. I was ready to chicken out, but Tonya proceeded to the edge of the boat undeterred and stuck her regulator in her mouth, held her mask, and also rolled backward off the boat. So, like a duckling following its mother, I checked my regulator one last time, sat on the edge of the boat, and did my backward roll into the ocean. I swam to Tonya, who was still at the surface. When

I was within an arm's reach, I signaled downward with my thumb—communicating in PADI sign language I was ready for us to descend.

Holding the inflator hose, I squeezed the button to deflate my BCD and descended below the surface and gradually continued downward. I was surprised by how far I could see. José was easily visible at the bottom, so I glided to him while keeping my eyes on Tonya. Tonya struggled to descend, finding herself too buoyant in the saltwater, but eventually, she too started to ease downward.

As Tonya descended, I spotted a large barracuda gracefully moving in our direction. It glided toward us moving about fifteen feet in front of José and me. Meanwhile, Tonya was still struggling to lose her positive buoyancy, and little did she know a long, narrow fish with a creepy smile was moving in her direction. She signaled to me with the diving gesture that she was okay, without noticing that she was about to saddle onto the large creature. I pointed to the large fish and wiggled my hand signaling fish, but she cluelessly repeated her okay sign language back to me. I thought her fin was sure to smack its face, but right before impact the large fish dashed away.

Tonya came beside me, and we followed José. I was enamored by the spectacular colors of coral reefs below, elegant fish, and the surreal feeling of effortlessly gliding above it. My surroundings transformed like the images in a kaleidoscope as the ocean current continuously pushed us forward to the next vibrant scene. We moved away from the coral toward an underwater cliff. We were hovering above the white sand on the ocean floor but were peering out over the cliff into its dark black bottomless pit. I watched Tonya glide over the cliff and felt the urge to grab her to keep her from falling into the abyss, forgetting for a moment that we were submerged in water, hovering with neutral buoyancy. I watched her move back to José and continued to soak in my surroundings. I moved my feet forward, crossed my legs, and leaned back like I was in a recliner, and stared at this brand new world that had been hidden from me. I marveled at the variety, quantity, and beauty of the fish who seemed to care little about me, busy attending to their daily routines. I peered back toward the abyss, calculating its depth to be several hundred feet. After gawking at my surroundings for about a minute, I turned to see if Tonya was equally impressed.

But when I turned toward her, she was gone. José was gone. The visibility was so clear that I could see for a hundred feet or more, but as I looked left and right, there were no signs of them. I checked my depth finder and was startled to see that I was ninety feet deep, well below the thirty feet limit I had wanted to place on myself.

I began to panic. I thought about going to the surface but decided that would be a bad idea because it was likely they would never find me up there. I started to turn to look in the opposite direction than the current was taking me and immediately felt the force of the current trying to rip my mask from my face. I then started to hear an echoing *dong, dong* that sounded like it was coming from the direction behind me. (Later, I would learn this noise was caused by José banging a metal washer against his tank in hopes of getting my attention.) So, I turned completely against the current and started to kick my fins as hard as I could to propel myself. Then, I saw Tonya and José, like two small creatures in the distance, waving to me to swim back toward them and toward the direction of the shoreline.

I kicked with fury, but felt like I stayed in place from the force of the current. I lengthened my kicks, trying to gain more force, and gradually found myself moving closer to José and Tonya. Kick after kick I crept forward, finally reaching them and finding myself back to thirty feet depth with the current not nearly as strong. Although we spent more time near the shore surrounded by mysterious and mind-blowing creatures, like inflated puffer fish and tiny seahorses, I was relieved to stick my head out of the water and breathe without the assistance of an oxygen tank.

The rest of our dives were uneventful and nearly effortless. On the dive boats a crew double-checked our gear, assisted with getting us ready, and even helped us in the water if needed. The boat also would drop us off, and we would spend thirty or forty minutes riding the current thirty to sixty feet below the surface—seeing stunning coral and unique fish, sea turtles, lobsters, stingrays, and all types of sea life. When we would be running low on air, we would come to the surface where the boat would pick us up. There was no fighting against the current.

Even though the normal group dives were much easier, I treasured the experience of the first dive so much more. It taught me not just how to be prepared for a dive, but also served as a metaphor on how to be prepared and face life. Both in living and diving, we should…

❖ **Ride the waves and kick like hell against the current** – During my dive, in one moment, I was peacefully enjoying my surroundings and moving effortlessly, but then in an instant, I found myself ninety feet below the surface fighting against the current and nearly frozen in fear. How could something that seemed so pleasant one moment seem so scary the next? Likewise, on June 13, 2018, I was content with my work, my family, and my life, but on June 14, I was told I had cancer that appeared to have already metastasized. My work, my family, and my life were disrupted. One moment life is joyful, peaceful, and beautiful. But in an instant, it also can be scary, dark, and lonely. There are moments in life that felt like riding the waves of good fortune. And there are the moments I've kicked with all my might treading water. The lesson isn't to fret over what bad can happen. The lesson is to hold precious the good days and be willing to kick like hell during the bad ones.

❖ **Be willing to confront your fears** – Ocean life is full of a wide spectrum of organisms that come in all shapes, colors, and sizes. What can look bizarre and scary—a jellyfish, a shark, an eel, a stingray, a barracuda—can feel frightening and threatening. But when you study them closer, you appreciate that their uniqueness isn't a cause for fear, but a cause for awe and wonder, and a gift that adds to the richness of the ecosystem of the ocean. So too is the beauty and gift in the diversity of people who walk this earth with different beliefs, languages, sizes, and colors. The life lesson is instead of labeling and judging others who are different, take time to really get to know people who are different—those of a different race, religion, and sexual orientation than you in order to confront your fears and to find beauty in our differences.

❖ **Take measured risks** – Life isn't about extreme adventures or reckless risks. We didn't just jump into the ocean with scuba gear on and hope for the best. We took the time to become scuba certified and practiced our skills from the shore before going out on the boat. But at the same time, life is also about having the courage to jump into unknown waters at times with the confidence to know that your planning and preparation will help you find your way.

❖ **Keep a buddy by your side** – What I remember most about the dive is the fear of being alone, isolated, forgotten. A key rule of diving is to stay next to your dive buddy. I had broken the rule. I didn't do it deliberately. Yet because I wasn't purposely, deliberately committed to sticking together, I slowly drifted away. Life also has a way of causing us to drift from one another at times. Life often feels like this race of moving to the next thing— going to work, making dinner, getting kids to events, checking email, paying bills, mowing grass. In an effort to check things off the list, we fail to appreciate the list itself and the most important things on it—loving each other.

Although scuba diving and life come with inherent risks, those are best confronted and reduced with people you trust and love by your side. But diving, living, and loving are all active sports. Love is not just about a feeling. It's about doing. Falling in love is easy. Staying in love is the challenge. Much like in diving, you must be keenly aware of your surroundings, appreciative of the beauty that surrounds you, and willing to struggle and persevere when things don't go exactly as planned.

As I continued to wait on the pathology results, I felt helpless. And yet, I found myself not wanting to talk about my darkest feelings with anyone—including Tonya. I knew that Tonya was struggling emotionally since my diagnosis. She was puzzled, almost frustrated, to see how I could jump out of bed each morning and focus on work, kids, and normal routines—almost ignoring our circumstances. For her, cancer was an unforgiving ocean. She, I, and our two girls had been helplessly submerged in its depth. And she was left to watch me be carried away by its relentless current into its abyss. In contrast, I would glance at the abyss and look away—pretending I barely noticed the tug of the endless pit. My focus was not on the darkness in the distance or the creatures that lurked in the shadow, but on the light permeating all around me and the beauty of my surroundings that the light revealed.

When I did feel overwhelmed and haunted by the mysterious darkness, I didn't want to talk about it. Admitting my feelings of fear and despair felt like I was weak and surrendering to the gravitational pull of the bottomless hole. I also knew that Tonya was already having a hard time coping, so I wanted to stay positive for her. But the truth is that by attempting to "protect her" from my feelings, from my fears, I wasn't guarding her from the pain, I was letting her tread water helplessly alone. I was breaking not only the rules of diving, but the rules of marriage. I wasn't staying connected to my buddy.

More than ever, Tonya needed my hand, and I was floating away.

CHAPTER 20:

STAY STRONG

Life Lesson: The measure of strength in life
is not how much one can lift.
It's what one can carry.

Dr. Helft contacted me to discuss the results of the pathology report. The tests showed the tissue samples from my lymph nodes and other samples taken were all benign. It was wonderful news—a huge relief—mainly because of what they *didn't* find. Although the original tumor was still present, cancer had not progressed as badly as the PET/CT scan suggested. It didn't mean that the immunotherapy was working, but it also didn't categorically prove that it was *not* working. So, it meant that I could continue with my treatments. It meant that I still had hope.

I told myself that I could beat this thing. I told myself that I could do it. I could grind my teeth through pain. I could overcome hardship. I could fight back from weakness. I wanted to mark my face with war paint, grab a spear, and charge into the battle screaming—ready to pierce through the cancer that stood in my way.

"Stay strong." Those were the words of encouragement I heard the most from my father, Stan Fischer, a man who had been my role model for strength—both in his words and in his actions. As a kid, I was awed by the ease in which he could hit a towering pop fly as my little league coach. I was inspired by his stories of his courage and strength in serving in the Army. I respected his firm discipline and knew that "getting his belt" didn't mean that his pants were too loose. I loved that he had the imagination, talent, and strength to fix anything. His firm handshakes with his calloused hands were regular reminders of how he didn't shy away from hard work.

But I wasn't my dad. He was a man's man—he was someone who could cut down a tree, make a cabin out of its wood, hunt for a meal, and cook it over a fire that he could start with a couple of stones and sticks. Meanwhile, even when I was in my late twenties, I was the guy who could study the proper angle to land the tree, but never actually start the chainsaw. I could determine the square feet of the cabin, but not build a square inch of it.

I envied my dad's rugged exterior and respected his firm guidance. His stocky frame and thick forearms were reminders of his physical strength which, according to him, he developed from carrying five-gallon buckets of water on the small family farm where he grew up. Like my mom, I knew he had unconditional love for me, but I also knew my actions had consequences. If I was sad, scared, embarrassed, upset, angry, disappointed, or frustrated, I knew he was willing to listen, but I also knew the single question that mattered most to him was: "What are you going to do about it?" He didn't want me to become a victim of my circumstances. He wanted to give me agency to act. He acknowledged that life is full of disappointments and struggles, but taught me that it's *what I do* with that disappointment and how I face struggles that matters most.

When I was younger, I equated my dad's interests and skills in handyman work, fishing, and hunting with his toughness and manliness. Being able to shoot, skin, cook, and eat a rabbit didn't just seem like a hobby, it seemed like a connection to our ancestry where hunting was a part of survival. Hunting felt like some rite of passage or initiation that I needed to complete—some chapter in a Man School book that I had skipped for too long. I had taken a different path through life than my dad. He was a proud and talented blue-collar worker. I was a freshly ironed white-collar worker. Although he always seemed accepting of my interests, hunting felt like something that would make him proud. So, even when I was in my late twenties, when my dad talked about going on a rabbit hunting trip with a couple friends, I surprised both him and myself by asking if I could go along.

Dad chuckled at first, but then asked, "Are you serious?"

After I convinced him that I was interested in going with him, he genuinely seemed pleased to have me join them. He explained to me that he and his best friend, Gene, wanted to travel to another friend's cattle range in northern Missouri "because they had lots of rabbits." I really never questioned the motive or my father's rationale for driving ten hours to hunt for rabbits, which were quite plentiful throughout southern Indiana, even in his own backyard.

So, my journey into manhood started with an eight-hour truck ride with my dad and Gene to the small town of Hatfield, Missouri, just south of the Iowa border. By the time we arrived, I found myself ending the lyrics to some of the country songs on the radio, even though I had never heard them before this trip. As I stepped out of the truck and was welcomed with the strong scent of fresh cow manure, I realized I already missed the smell of beagles and deer jerky that had been trapped inside the small truck cab for eight hours.

I awoke the next morning to the sound of the other men rustling through their hunting gear. Dad was downstairs with Gene beginning to get dressed. Following the lead of the other men, I slid on my camouflage coveralls, laced up my boots, slid into an orange vest, and put on my orange stocking hat and camouflage gloves. I giggled for a moment at the irony of wearing camouflage and orange at the same time. I was going to comment on the logic of the inconsistent attire, but then reminded myself not to say anything stupid that might cause them to question having me with them with a loaded gun.

One by one we filed into the pickup truck, waited for the engine to warm, then pulled out of the drive of the old farmhouse. My eyes shut for a moment and then I found us stopping again. With the truck idling, Gene and Dad jumped out of the cab waiting for me to follow. As I exited the vehicle, I could hear the loud barking of the beagles in the nearby shed. The three dogs, each in their own distinct pitch, roared; the result almost sounded like a chorus of "Row, Row, Row Your Boat." The bass beagle would start with the first verse with deep, throaty "Aroroar," a second would follow as the tenor with a higher-pitched "Roar," and the third would chime in as soprano with an ear-piercing "Arrrr," and then it would repeat... "Aroroar, roar, arrr. Aroroar, roar, arr." I wanted to sing along adding, "...life is but a dream."

Dad, Gene, and I entered the shed where the beagles' singing echoed inside a small cattle trailer. As the dogs howled, Dad responded as if he understood every request. "Yes, I know..." He said sympathetically, "We'll let you stretch your legs in a bit." Carefully he released the latch of the gate, still holding the unlocked gate shut. He allowed the dark black nose of a beagle to emerge. As he continued slowly to open the gate, the snout of the beagle appeared, followed by his head. Dad promptly grabbed a leash, clipped it on the collar of the beagle, then allowed the gate to open—only until the first beagle leaped to the ground, then he shut it again quickly. Dad handed me the leash and ordered, "Here, take Bluegill out to walk around."

Chuckling at the dog's name that would clearly make him think he was a fish, I grabbed the leash and laughed as his animated movement successfully tangled up the leash. I bent down to untangle the leash when suddenly Bluegill dashed around my leg, making me part of the entanglement. I took a moment to free myself and the beagle from the puzzle then looked back to the trailer to see Buster and Lucky make similar excited exits.

Buster and Lucky dashed back and forth with their nose on the ground leading their momentum. After admiring the enthusiasm of the other two beagles, I looked back at Bluegill. He stood with one leg pointed outward beside a bucket near the back of the trailer. Dad glanced over and said sharply, "Brad, take him somewhere else to piss!" Embarrassed, I pulled Bluegill away and walked him to the open field.

Bluegill, Buster, and Lucky all seemed to enjoy what they knew would be the short-lived freedom. Instinctively, by having the leash attached, they seemed to know that it wasn't quite time to start the hunt. They meandered around for a while marking their territory every few feet until, acceptingly, they allowed Gene and Dad to put them in the homemade metal pen in the back of the truck. As they closed the grated door on the beagles, Buster gave two quick howls. Again, Dad, as if he understood the bark perfectly, assured the curious beagle, "We're about there. Just a few more minutes." As I closed the tailgate, the beagles barked again. This time, I chimed in, "I know… I'm eager too." Dad and I glanced at each other, exchanging smiles.

As we drove a few miles to our hunting destination, I marveled at the vast open rolling fields filled with prairie grass. Glancing out the window, I was amazed by how far I could see. There were hardly any buildings and few trees to obstruct my vision. It certainly was peaceful.

My moment of meditation was interrupted as the truck came to a stop in the middle of a field beside an electric fence. As the truck stopped, the beagles immediately started in with their familiar chorus: "Aroroar, roar, arrr." I hopped out of the truck and walked toward the three vocalists following Dad and Gene. One by one the beagles made their exit, this time without being restricted by the leashes. The dogs wasted no time in beginning their pursuit. Their noses immediately dropped to the cold ground, and the dogs moved forward as we could hear them sniff.

I grabbed a twelve-gauge shotgun and some shotgun shells from the back of the pickup. Although I had shot the gun various times at targets when I was younger, it had been several years since I had used a gun. I glanced at the other men hoping I could copy their movements in loading the gun. I saw them each slide a shell into their shotgun and press a lever to chamber it. I grabbed the shells feigning confidence and began chambering shells one by one. I slid the fourth shell into the loading slot and slid the lever to chamber it as I had the others. In doing so, a shell flew from the release chamber landing beside my dad's foot, coldly reminding me that the gun only holds three shells. My dad glanced at me with a combination of bewilderment and pity. Trying not to draw attention to the fact that I had faltered with the weapon, I picked up the extra shell and slid it into my pocket.

I pulled my orange hat down to cover my ears from the cold air and began walking with the others. The beagles continued moving forward along a small creek. Each of their tails swung side to side, showing their intensity and thrill of finding the scent they were born to trace. With Buster in the lead, the beagles disappeared into the heavy brush.

I glanced at my gun and verified that the safety was on. I reminded myself of my most important rules of the hunt: 1) Don't shoot any of the beagles, 2) Don't shoot the other hunters, and 3) Don't shoot myself. In watching the men train and talk to the beagles, I knew if I broke rule #1, I also would need to break rule #3 or my hunting partners would break rule #2. It was clear that the beagles were like royalty. We were peasants along during their hunt to help in any way possible. Seeing the dogs' devotion to the task at hand, I vowed not to let the kings down.

As we walked through the woods, my previous thoughts of feeling like Elmer Fudd—a character from the *Bugs Bunny* cartoon that made me laugh as a kid because of his determination, but struggle with hunting rabbits—began to fade. Instead, I felt like a warrior ready for battle. "Bring me a rabbit," I whispered to the beagles with impatience and excitement. Only fifteen or twenty minutes had elapsed and already I had the urge to pull the trigger. Now all I needed was the furry little head of that wascally wabbit. (Okay, the Elmer thoughts hadn't fully faded.)

The rustle of us walking through the brush was interrupted by a quick, single "Aroroar" from Buster. I stood silent, wondering if I had only imagined the howl. Again, Buster howled "Aroroar." My pulse quickened and I tightened my grip on the gun. His tail began swinging side to side even quicker. Upon hearing his howl, Bluegill and Lucky stopped their pursuit and began snorting the ground next to Buster. After a few sniffs, Lucky made a quick one-syllable outburst: "Roar." Lucky, too, followed with a single "Arrr."

I peered at the three wagging tails in the brush moving forward. From within the brush their repetitive howls interrupted the peaceful surroundings. Hearing the excitement of the beagles' voices, my heart began to race.

"Get ready," Dad ordered like a general commanding his troops. "Brad, cover that field!"

Aye, aye, Sergeant, I thought, quickly manning my post. The beagles' howls continued to repeat with shortened intervals. Their voices grew quieter, not because of their intensity, but because of their increased distance from me.

I heard a rustle in the bushes on the other side of a sharp decline in the terrain. Obstructed by a collection of trees, I moved diagonally toward the noise, wondering if one of the beagles had not followed the others. On my second step, suddenly a rabbit appeared in midair above the brush—leaping from his hideout. The image was fleeting but unmistakable. With my gun resting on my shoulder, the rabbit seemed to look at me with mockery in his eyes. In the flash of fur that flew above the brush, I'm certain the rabbit had his middle finger extended—affirming his arrogance of his bold move.

I flipped the shotgun off my shoulder and caught the barrel with my left hand. As I raised the stock of the gun against my right shoulder, I slid the safety to the off position and moved the sights of the gun left and right, looking for the enemy. The varmint had vanished.

As if I were a general calling for backup, I yelled to the other men and beagles, "I spotted a rabbit!" The beagles continued to move away from my location uninterested. I continued to survey my surroundings hoping I would catch another glimpse of the furry-headed villain. I began kicking nearby logs and brushes hoping to scare the sly, pointy-eared enemy out of his hole. I walked several yards back and forth, rustling through the thick brush. Nothing. The rabbit had clearly escaped. Since the beagles and the men continued moving forward, I decided to abort this mission and join them in their pursuit. I left the area feeling as if I had lost the battle; however, I was even more prepared for the war.

Buster, Lucky, and Bluegill continued with their yelping. For a moment, I questioned their instinctive pursuit. After all, they clearly hadn't traced the scent of the rabbit that had flashed before my eyes. However, as their howling became more intense and I saw their tails beat against the bushes, I became convinced that they knew what they were doing.

I positioned myself in an open field and watched the beagles work inside the brush. Their howling became more intense and animated. Their tails swatted the brush with such fury that I could see the tips of their tails had turned red with blood. Their noses seemed to pull the rest of their body forward. I stood stiff with anticipation and awe as the beagles bellowed through the crescendo of their symphony.

This time I would not let the beagles down. I would be ready. I slid the safety to the off position and held the gun outward, waiting for the rabbit. The beagles had disappeared into the brush. Their voices grew louder and louder as they advanced toward me. I could tell that they were in hot pursuit and that I stood in the perfect position for the kill.

And then it happened. The rabbit emerged from the brush with a sideways leap, scurrying to escape the ruckus of the three howlers. I aimed at the rabbit as he made a second leap in the opposite direction. I gripped the weapon tightly and squeezed the trigger. "POW!" The gun recoiled into my shoulder. I continued to look at the target and watched the rabbit make a ninety-degree leap in the opposite direction, dodging the spray of BBs and momentarily disappearing into the tall grass. Clearly this was a skilled rabbit—one with ninja-like moves capable of evading my accurate shot. I remained focused and determined.

The rabbit appeared again in a leap above the grass. I aimed again and fired. "POW!" The rabbit dropped into the grass, disappearing again. I approached carefully, still taking aim. As I grew closer I saw the rabbit lying on his side, motionless, and lifeless.

I stood above the rabbit with a mixture of reverence for the life I had taken and a swelling of pride in actually hitting my target. As my dad approached me, he smiled and gave me a pat on the back. I took a moment to celebrate with the beagles—wanting to howl with them hoping they would somehow understand how masterful I thought they were in their pursuit. I stared at the lifeless rabbit and looked at my dad wondering if he was going to pick it up or what exactly happened next. But then I realized he wanted me to answer the question—"What are you going to do about it?"—for myself.

"That's your rabbit. You gotta carry it," he told me, then added with a warm smile, "I'll show you how to clean it later." He said it with a look of love and support, but I also knew he was serious.

Pulling the trigger was the easy part. Even into my late twenties, he was teaching me that my actions had consequences. And, if I was prepared to pull the trigger on a rabbit, I also would need to be prepared to kill it, carry it, clean it, cook it, and eat it. My dad handed me a plastic bag. I reluctantly slid the rabbit inside and placed it in the back pocket of my hunting vest. It was my responsibility to carry the weight of my decisions.

As I stood next to Dad as an adult in those fields, I also began to understand that it wasn't my skills that kept me from being a man. It was my view of what it meant to be a man. These were strong and rugged men whose experiences I admired. They knew how to train and command beagles, had accurate shots, and could clean a rabbit in a matter of minutes, but none of that made them good men. My dad was strong, not because he had carried five-gallon buckets. He was strong because of his mental toughness. And, furthermore, it wasn't his strength that made him a wonderful father and a great man. It was his tenderness. It was love. I knew regardless whether or not I shared his hobbies and skills, he was proud of me and loved me.

I started to realize that the fly balls that he hit me as my little league coach really weren't that high, but his devotion to his players reached beyond the clouds. His service in the military wasn't about his hatred for the enemy or unmatched courage or desire to kill, but about his love for his country. His firm discipline and using his belt wasn't guided by anger but instead by his endless belief in me and knowing I could make better choices. He wasn't naturally gifted at fixing things as I assumed; he was just persistent in his tinkering and solving problems because he wanted to help our family and others. Even his firm handshakes didn't only remind me of the strength in his hands, but always showed me the warmth in his heart. And, driving ten hours to go rabbit hunting in Missouri with old friends had little to do with the quantity or size of Missouri rabbits, but everything with the bond these men had formed.

Dad taught me that the strength of a person is really rooted in their love for others. It is love that made (and continues to make) me want to endure the physical and emotional pain of cancer, to shake away the weakness that came with chemotherapy. It is love that made me want to erase the sorrow from Tonya's expression and freeze those smiles on my kids' faces. It is love that made me know that I was not fighting the disease alone and that I had others lifting me up every time I fell. It is love that made me feel I still had more to give of myself to others and to believe my work here surely wasn't done.

Alone, I am weak. But because of others, because of love, I am strong. And even though I cannot control what cancer ultimately does to me, I do get to control my attitude and what action I take. And so, the question I must continue to ask myself is simply, *What am I going to do about it?*

CHAPTER 21:

SPEAK FROM YOUR HEART

Life Lesson: Say what you mean. Mean what you say.
But don't be mean in what you say.

WHEN LIZZIE WAS SIX YEARS old, I asked what she wanted to be when she grew up. She promptly replied, "A pet shop owner." She then added, "And no parents would be allowed."

In truth, she had said, "And no *parrots* would be allowed," but I had misunderstood her pronunciation of the word. So, thinking she had just banned myself and all parents from her future business, I sharply responded, "Well, that's rude. Why aren't parents allowed?"

She, thinking I was repeating the word parrots, answered, "Because they are so talkative and plain weird."

Although I candidly recognized some truth in what I thought was her assessment of my silly behavior, I still thought they were pretty harsh and hateful words for a six-year-old. So, being rather disturbed by her bossy language, I scolded her saying that was not a nice thing to say.

Lizzie couldn't make sense of my disagreement or my distaste for her colorful criticism of parrots. The conversation continued to spiral downward for several minutes. I pleaded my case of why *parents* should be allowed; she remained unflappable, insisting *parrots* would not be admitted. The more we argued, the more each side dug into their position. With a wounded voice, I finally shared simply how much her mom and I would like to come to her store.

She sat quietly for a moment with a puzzled expression on her face that then shifted to a smile and said, "You and Mom can come! I said *parrots* aren't allowed."

Communication is hard.

When I think about how I communicate, I think about the two competing voices often inside my head: the voice of Analytical Brad and the voice of Emotional Brad. Emotional Brad is the dreamer, the visionary, the storyteller, the listener, the laugher, the crier. Analytical Brad is the problem solver, the professional, the critiquer, the challenger, the implementer, the doer. Analytical Brad hears an idea, questions the details to better understand it, dissects it into the pros and cons, makes a verdict on its overall merit, identifies the challenges that would need to be overcome during implementation, lists out the milestones and necessary steps, and then goes to work to transform the idea into reality. Meanwhile, Emotional Brad is the guy for after hours. The guy who would tell stories about playing Shit Purse and memories of mistakenly walking into a stranger's home. Emotional Brad is the guy who likes to make up dance moves to make his girls laugh. Emotional Brad soaks and savors in the moment of laughing and enjoying peoples' stories and company.

My view of effective communication has changed. Before my diagnosis, I thought good communication was primarily about concisely presenting an idea, using logic and reasoning to make a case, and about persuading others. In short, I thought my job—and the world—mostly needed Analytical Brad. But as I reflect on my life and on my failures of good communication, I realize that Emotional Brad has always been better than Analytical Brad at the following.

- **Listening to learn** – Good communication begins with a willingness and earnest desire to listen to learn from others. Before we try to convince others of an idea, we must be willing to first understand someone else's idea and be willing to be convinced or persuaded by those ideas. Even if we disagree with someone's position, we must allow ourselves to soak in their perspective and try to see it from their angle.

  I was so focused on thinking on what I should say to correct Lizzie's behavior for banning parents and describing them as "talkative and weird" that I didn't take the time to deeply listen to what she was saying or try hard enough to understand why she was saying it.

- **Making an emotional connection** – We must be willing to admit mistakes, tell stories that may be embarrassing or stories that are empowering, and be willing to share a part of our soul. When I think about how people have persuaded or influenced me and others on something, it is often not through facts and figures, it's about an emotional story/hook that is not just sensible to my head, but appeals to the heart. Think about JFK's call to the nation to put a man on the moon or MLK Jr.'s "I Have a Dream" speech. Or, consider Apple's incredible comeback as a company that began with their release of the iPod in 2001. They didn't make the case that the iPod had better specs compared to other MP3 players. They simply said they could put a thousand songs in our pocket.

Likewise, only when I openly shared my disappointment of not being allowed in the pet shop did Lizzie finally understand why I was upset.

❖ **Being open and honest with others** – First and foremost, be honest with yourself and others. Tell people you appreciate them and tell people when something is upsetting and frustrating. Most people can sniff out a fake. They can sense false praises, manufactured anger, and forced laughs. Be yourself. Be real.

Although confronting Lizzie about her policy of banning parents created an argument, not voicing my concern could have created an even deeper misunderstanding or even resentment. By openly talking about the issue we eventually were able to clarify the problem.

As I found myself "floating away" from Tonya, I realized it was mostly because I failed to allow Emotional Brad into the conversations.

Analytical Brad wanted to make the rational argument, wanted to talk about solutions, wanted to have contingency plans. Analytical Brad wanted to follow the facts and be prepared—even for the worst outcomes.

Emotional Brad also wanted to protect Tonya. Talking about my prognosis or my feelings felt like I was spreading the suffering. Finally, one day I awoke in the middle of the night hearing Tonya crying into a handful of tissues. The reality of the situation became pitifully clear to me. There I was—right beside her physically. But there she was—alone. Emotionally alone. Sobbing. When I asked her about it, she said she often cried at night—trying to hide it from me during the day because she wanted to protect *me*. So there we were—two people trying to protect each other by hiding our emotions from each other.

We would do anything for the other. We hated to see the other suffer. But by trying to protect each other, we were pulling apart—rather than pulling together. We were like two people on different ends of a rope tugging. Not talking about our fear, frustration, or sadness didn't shield the other from the emotions. The elephant was always in the room. But not acknowledging its presence felt like we had to carry the weight of it all alone.

I certainly remain a student, not an expert, of good communication. But I do know this: Our time on this earth is limited. Life is delicate. One thing that cancer has taught me is that above all, we must be *open* with people.

Yes, communication is hard. When I was on chemotherapy, I found it difficult to organize and summarize all the thoughts and details that swarmed my brain. But I know now that all the minutiae that fills my head matters little compared to the love that fills my heart. The love I have felt has made me realize that being good at communication is not about being an expert orator. It's not even about effectively conveying all that is in my head. Effective communication is ultimately about caring and connecting—and that is true not just in our bedrooms at home but also in our boardrooms at work.

When I was first diagnosed with cancer with such a bleak prognosis, I felt the sands in my hour glass rushing from the top to the bottom with no way to slow it. I felt an enormous surge of what I needed to do and say. I needed to tell Tonya several passwords so she could properly manage our home finances. I needed to tell her about the new way I was organizing our family photos. I needed to make sure she knew the trick to start our leaf blower. Likewise, I felt there were a million life lessons I needed to share with my girls that ranged from dating, to going to college, to being good people. (It's what compelled me to start writing.) But in the end, truthfully what I want the girls and Tonya to know more than anything is how much I love them.

After all, I'm still hoping that one day Lizzie lets me into her pet shop.

CHAPTER 22:

CHOOSE TO BE KINDER

Life Lesson: *It's not all right to just be all right. You must also be kind.*

GEORGE SAUNDERS DELIVERED THE CONVOCATION speech at Syracuse University for the class of 2013. What advice does a bestselling American writer give to some of our nation's best young minds entering the workforce? *Try to be kinder.* Below is an excerpt from his speech published in the *New York Times*' 6th Floor blog.

> *"What I regret most in my life are failures of kindness. Those moments when another human being was there, in front of me, suffering, and I responded…sensibly. Reservedly. Mildly. Or, to look at it from the other end of the telescope: Who, in your life, do you remember most fondly, with the most undeniable feelings of warmth? Those who were kindest to you, I bet. It's a little facile, maybe, and certainly hard to implement, but I'd say, as a goal in life, you could do worse than: Try to be kinder."*

As a parent, kindness is something I find myself endlessly trying to teach my kids. "Say 'please' and 'thank you.' Treat others as you would want to be treated. Include others in your game. Shake an opponent's hand after the soccer game. Lower your voice. Listen and learn from others." Even as I correct their behavior, there are moments—like when I trip over their shoes and backpacks as I walk in the door— that words of kindness aren't rolling off my tongue. I keep hoping for that day when I can put a checkmark next to the home learning objective: Be kind. But no matter how many lessons I give, there is another lesson waiting.

Most people agree that kindness is an important quality to teach our children, but do we put a premium on this trait like other attributes, like wealth or intelligence? I tested this by asking several people a simple question: "Would you rather be richer, smarter, or kinder?" Very few chose kinder. It's possible that my small sampling of people are heartless overachievers or have already reached the maximum limit of human kindness. Perhaps the sampling is not reflective of how most would answer, but I'm guessing most would not put kinder at the top. Being kinder seems too subjective—just a little squishy. We live in a world with winners and losers, where we strive to find our "competitive advantage." We recognize and reward hard work and sharp minds. Don't the nice guys always finish last? And, really...haven't we reached a satisfactory level of kindness already? Is Saunders's message of "try to be kinder" really a message that will appropriately guide recent college graduates?

If I'm honest with myself, before my cancer diagnosis, I would have picked "smarter" myself. After all, how great would it be to work on answers to questions to help others like "What is the best approach to solve world hunger?" or "What causes cancer and how can it be prevented and cured?" Or, at minimal, I could finally answer questions that baffled me most of my life like "Why do dogs understand what I'm feeling better than most humans?" or "How do you fold fitted sheets?"

When I think of kindness, I often think of my mom, the most giving person I know—a person I respect more than just about anyone—even though she never attended college, grew up poor, and seemed to never desire accumulating wealth. I've never met anyone else that genuinely finds joy in cooking and cleaning for others. My girls have come to expect a fresh bowl of vegetable soup—or GGS as they call it, which stands for Grandma's Great Soup—prepared specially for them every time they visit. She regularly visits nursing homes and has a way of gravitating to those who are sick or in need. Even while she was recovering from a partial hip replacement, she would stay busy cooking meals for others. She doesn't approach any of these as sacrifices or burdens. Serving others is her own personal hobby.

As I've come to terms with my diagnosis and hard realization that all our time here is limited, I often think about what I regret most about the life that I've lived. And, I have to admit, Saunders captures my sentiments precisely: "What I regret most in my life are failures of kindness. Those moments when another human being was there, in front of me, suffering, and I responded...sensibly. Reservedly. Mildly."

My regrets are from actions that date back to middle school to moments just months ago. I am still haunted by getting up from a lunch table during middle school with a group of friends as another guy sat down beside us. I didn't lead the betrayal and didn't want to do it, but I didn't have the courage to break from the pack. I regret being rather selfish and self-centered (in hindsight) with a girl I dated in college. I regret not spending more time with my grandma when she was in the nursing home. I regret not reaching out more frequently to my brother, Mark, when his wife was battling breast cancer. I regret not volunteering more frequently at places like Riley Children's Hospital, even after I saw the anguish in the eyes of other parents trying to comfort their sick kid. I regret turning my cheek to the homeless in Indianapolis, pretending they didn't exist. I regret not being more vocal and active in supporting causes that will matter long after I've gone—like protecting the environment. To everyone I wronged and to everyone who has endured suffering while I stood silent, I truly am sorry. You deserved better.

I often think about where I've spent most of my time. And, the short answer is I've spent most of my time at work. I often justified the time I spent working on weekends and evenings to myself because I believed the work I am doing matters. I know the project I'm working on will benefit teachers, which will help students gain new knowledge, skills, or experiences that will ultimately give them a brighter future. But through this persistence and dedication to bring a brighter *future* to our students, too often I lost sight of bringing a brighter *day* to the people in my life. And, when my time comes, I doubt few will stand up and talk about my technical skills or the projects I completed. As George Saunders contends, the memories (good or bad) will be the way I have made people feel.

Kindness certainly consists of many small moments—saying "good morning" or "thank you," listening sympathetically to a frustration, or making someone laugh when they most need it. But being kind is also about doing what is right, even when it's not what is easy or popular. It's about having the courage to disagree with others' ideas when necessary, the compassion to defend and assist a person being ridiculed or someone in need, taking a stand and action on a cause that is important, and the confidence to believe that you can help. For a quality that is a little "squishy" to talk about, it's rock hard to keep practicing.

To be clear, I don't think financial wealth or intelligence are the enemies or even the competition for kindness. This isn't a zero-sum game where we must withdraw from our intelligence or wealth in order to deposit in the kindness column. However, I do think that the danger of more wealth and education/intelligence is that we can falsely tell ourselves that these attributes somehow make us better than those with less. And, ultimately, it's what we do with our blessings that makes all the difference. After all, wealth and intelligence are needed to help solve world hunger and cure cancer. I simply would argue that in order to obtain such lofty visions—as well as most things in life that bring satisfaction—they must be rooted and guided first and foremost by kindness.

Try to be kinder.

As I reflect on others' lives and then my own, I recognize that Saunders's message wasn't just good advice for college graduates, it's good advice to me and all of us. We can all choose to be kinder.

CHAPTER 23:

THE DUCK & FROG SHOW

Life Lesson: Parenting is about laughing, learning, and love. With a little duck, *you will spend each day* quacking *up, being* hoppy, *and creating un*frog*ettable memories.*

NOTHING IN MY LIFE HAS shown me the power of love more than the love for my kids. Although parenting is about giving, what you gain is immeasurable. The best way for me to share my own views of parenting and lessons I've learned is to simply share my letter to Anna Mae and Lizzie that I hope guides them when I am gone.

Dear Anna Mae and Lizzie,

Do the two of you remember The Duck and Frog Show? *I sure hope you do. "Ladies and gentlemen, boys and girls of alllll ages,* The Duck and Frog Show *will be beginning in five minutes!" I would proclaim, using my best imitation*

of a circus master of ceremonies. The novelty and original-
ity of my performances had already run its course with your
mother, so she would give me a polite smile and shake her
head with a mixture of amusement and annoyance at my
theatrics. But the crowd I was really trying to bait—the two
of you when you were about two and four years old—would
react with excitement, which I thought was testimony to the
craft I had improved with multiple performances. After all,
getting your attention was no easy task considering that I
was interrupting your "busy schedules" of pretending to be
the teachers at Beanie Boo Preschool with your stuffed animals scattered in a circle for story time. At times, I would
remind you that the cost for admission required you to have
all your toys picked up. So, as the instructors of Beanie Boo
Preschool, you would quickly call for quiet time and place the
students into a basket.

In case you don't remember... To the average person,
Duck and Frog were mere washcloths that doubled as hand
puppets of—yep, you guessed it—a duck and a frog. (In
hindsight, the stage names I created for them could have
used a little work.) Nonetheless, on bath nights, Duck and
Frog were stars of a production that rivaled the best of
any Broadway show—at least to the critics that attended.
Instead of settling into the seats of a theater in Manhattan,
however, these critics—the two of you—would climb into
the tub taking your seats, which also happened to partially
submerge you into water and soapsuds.

Both of you would spend a moment dipping your arms into the suds, concentrating on avoiding the temptation of splashing too much, since that had created quite a mess on a previous show, and caused the MC (me) to add a new restriction on splashing during performances (and any bath time in general). With the two of you situated, I would slide my hands into the puppets and watch your big brown eyes, Anna Mae, and your glistening green eyes, Lizzie, stare at me waiting for the stars to take the imaginary stage.

"Ladies and gentlemen, boys and girls of allllll ages..." I would roar again, "Put your hands together for Duck and Frog!" And with the supportive clapping of their favorite fans, Duck and Frog took the stage. Their act was an impromptu bit that mimicked a late-night variety show. They sang songs, did magic tricks, told jokes, pretended to be boxers, invited guests, and regularly asked their favorite fans—the two of you—to participate with them—singing along, assisting with the magic trick, doing the rimshot sound effects on jokes, or serving as the referee in the boxing matches.

Duck was the mischievous one. For example, after the hearty introduction of The Duck and Frog Show, *occasionally only Frog would pop his head above the side of the tub. Frog would thank the crowd for coming, but then ask if they had seen Duck. Meanwhile, Duck would slowly pop his head up directly behind Frog. The two of you would scream at Frog. "He's right behind you!" Frog would look backward, but right before he was able to turn his head, Duck would disappear downward out of sight of the audience—and presumably out of view from Frog. Frog would turn back to face the two of you saying he was not there, and as he did, Duck would appear again—only this time he was shimmering left and right behind Frog, like he was dancing on hot coals. You both would crack up laughing. And the harder you laughed, the more Duck in the background doubled-over as if he was laughing. Frog, though, oblivious to it all, would ask what in the world was so funny? The more puzzled he became, the more you would laugh. The show would go on with Duck hiding from Frog, and Frog looking for Duck. Although Duck playfully teased Frog, he never tried to hurt his feelings. In fact, he silently cheered for him—encouraging the crowd to applaud—making Frog take a bow for what he thought was his own charm and talent. And, at the end of the show, Duck and Frog would always take a bow on stage together, as friends, knowing they had yet another great performance.*

I don't recall the date that Duck and Frog retired as performers. There was no final act, no final bow. They slowly became a little less funny, a little too cheesy for their audience. And the reruns eventually did get old—not only for the two of you, but for me, the guy who had his hands stuffed into their necks. If I recall correctly, The Duck and Frog Show *was replaced by a series called* Will It Float?, *a show about making predictions on whether or not something will or will not float.*

But that show too was canceled. And soon bath time was

replaced with showers. And in a blink of an eye, my audi-ence—the two of you—went from toddlers to little girls to budding young ladies. And along the way, the bedtime role of the creator of The Duck and Frog Show *and* Will it Float?, *the same guy who walked the floors for hours at night cra-dling each of you when you were teething, colicky, or scared, the guy who made up silly stories at bedtime, the person who would struggle to stay awake reading* Goodnight Moon, *and the dad who loved hearing you both read* Chicken Said Cluck, *became much smaller and smaller. I started to settle for a brief hug and a warm "I love you" as you disappeared into your bedroom.*

When did time begin to evaporate?

I worried deeply about being a dad. My biological clock certainly had been ready for a while. I was thirty-three. (Shouldn't wisdom come with age?) I worked in education, was surrounded by nieces and nephews I loved, and was mar-ried to someone I knew would be a wonderful mother. And yet, I still felt so unprepared. I read parenting books, partici-pated in parenting classes to learn important skills like which way to position the diaper, and eagerly sought the counsel of friends and family. But I was terrified. I was afraid I would place your car seat in my trunk and then get distracted and leave you there. I worried that your heavy head might break away from your neck because I didn't properly position my hand under your head when holding you. I feared I wouldn't cut your hot dog into small enough pieces and you would choke. And beyond physical care, I worried that I would not be good at being there for you emotionally. I feared that I would be aloof. That I would in turn make you become alienated, bitter, and mean. I thought a new baby in our home might make my best friend, Tonya, no longer be my buddy. I worried that you wouldn't love me. And, in truth, I worried that I might not love you.

I felt so unprepared to be a dad.

And, I was right. Not about the trunk thing, or the head snapping away from the neck, the hot dog, lack of love, or really about any of the scenarios that ran through my mind. I was wrong about all of that. But I was right that I was unprepared.

I wasn't prepared to know how to handle a colicky baby. (Nothing in those books worked!) I wasn't prepared for both of you to test the limits of what you could get away with at such an early age and for you to continue to test limits still today. I wasn't prepared for not knowing my own boundaries at times (which is why I so often say, "Go ask your mom"). And, I certainly had no idea how much drama comes with two middle-school-aged girls. I also didn't know how tired kids would make me feel. How frustrated, sad, helpless, or angry you could make me feel.

But I also had no idea how both of your tiny hands grabbing my finger for the first time, how hearing your laughs—both when you were infants and still today—would make me feel. I had no idea how proud, or how happy, or how much love you could make me feel.

I definitely have made my share of mistakes as a parent. It is by far the most difficult job I've ever had. But it is also without a doubt the part of my life I am most proud. My heart feels full and my life seems worthwhile by seeing the two of you become the people you have already become. And nothing fuels my desire to live more than the desire to see who you will become in the future.

I want to promise that I will be there for you—that regardless of what life throws at you, I will be there to listen. To laugh with you. To cry with you. To cheer you on. And to guide you the best I can. I want to be there for you as you face the struggles through your teenage years, college years, and help you find your footing as young adults.

And yet, I can't make that promise. I know that. You know that. As optimistic and hopeful as I want to be, the odds remain stacked against me. If cancer does get the best of me, I want you to remember that even after my physical presence here vanishes, I remain a part of the family. I remain with you. I know things will be hard as you navigate life. Really hard. You will feel angry. Scared. Lonely. Forgotten. Broken. It will be tempting to quit. To find excuses. To surrender and become a prisoner of the numbness and the pain.

But you are my lions. My bears. Remember, being brave is not about the absence of fear, sadness, or worry. It's about being willing to do what is necessary—what is right—even when you face those emotions. So, although your world may feel shattered, you must find the pieces to put back together.

The goal isn't to reassemble the fragments in hopes of assembling the family you once had. It is to have the strength and the vision to create something different. Not necessarily better. Or worse. But something beautiful. Your goal isn't to make me proud. Your mom will need you, and I hope you will help her and each other. But honestly, the goal isn't even to make her proud. Your goal—your challenge—is to make yourselves proud.

And, if you both become mothers someday, I would love to be able to introduce your kids to The Duck and Frog Show. *But if I'm not able to be here, feel free to steal my material. Or, even better, create your own routine. Find a way to learn alongside your own kids. To set your own limits. To laugh with them. But most of all, to love them. And when you feel like you need me most, picture me as Duck, the silly sidekick with a big smile standing right behind you—perhaps out of sight and reach—but cheering you on in all that you do.*

With all my love,
Dad

CHAPTER 24:

GONE

Life Lesson: Our time here is limited. Our impact is limitless.

"GONE." THAT WAS THE WORD I wanted to hear as I sat in the recovery room in the gastroenterology suite at the IU Health University Hospital in August 2020. I was still fading in and out of focus from the anesthesia for my endoscopy and colonoscopy. But even though I was barely lucid, my brain was able to dial into that single word. *Gone.*

I want these tumors to be gone.

It was about fourteen months earlier that I had been in the same recovery room after what I thought was a precautionary check for acid reflux-type symptoms and some stomach pains. The news that day had forever changed my life.

After eight rounds of chemotherapy, eighteen rounds of immunotherapy, three surgeries, and countless tests, I awoke to look into the face of Dr. Rex again. Over the last fourteen months, I trained myself to keep my emotions as level as possible to any news. No growth to minimal growth in the original tumors would be good. If there was a large growth in the original tumors or new tumors...well, I would continue with the plan and hope for the best. Either way, I would accept the news and move forward. But a third option would always slide into my head. I had read enough about immunotherapy to know that there were some remarkable cases of patients who saw their tumors vanish. These cases were the exceptions, but they were possible. I didn't want to build false hopes for myself, but I found myself letting that wishful thinking of being one of the lucky patients creep into my mind.

Dr. Rex had a look of bewilderment on his face as he began to share the news. "I was not able to see the original tumor. I only saw necrotic tissue instead. I also did not see any new tumors." He said it reluctantly, as if he wasn't believing the very words he muttered. His expression mirrored one of disbelief and caution. He seemed genuinely shocked by the results—even ordering another test—this time an endoscopy ultrasound. Again, they did not find any cancer. As Dr. Rex shared the news, I had to repeat the words to make sure I heard it correctly. There were no visual tumors. They only found scar tissue in my stomach, esophagus, and lymph node outside my stomach—all where the cancer was before. All the cancer that they had seen before was no longer there!

It was gone.

There was still so much I didn't know. I didn't know if it was gone everywhere. (Doctors can never prove that you don't have cancer. They can only prove you *do* have cancer.) I didn't know if it meant I would continue on treatment or not. I didn't know if the original tumors would come back or if new tumors would appear.

What I did know is that it was great news and that I was blessed. I felt such relief, joy, and gratitude. I was given a chance to do those things that felt out of reach only fourteen months prior. Maybe—just maybe—I would be able to be there for my girls a little longer after all.

I hadn't become the image of that person I thought was my fate—the shrinking body in a bed waiting for the disease to run its course. So, this was truly cause for celebration. I wanted to dance with all my friends, uninhibited, showing them that I was still here. I wanted to dance because I could.

And I wanted to cry.

None of this felt fair. None of this was fair. There were people way more deserving than me who have faced a different fate. I thought of my nephew, precious little Paul. I thought of a woman who cheered me on since my diagnosis even after losing her husband, a kind, loving man who was the father of a special needs son. I thought of a brilliant research doctor who was committed to serving others who succumbed to the disease. I thought of a woman in her early thirties who started immunotherapy for gastric cancer similar to mine around the same time as I did—in the same hospital, treated by the same doctors—who had already passed.

I thought of all the friends, relatives, colleagues, and the sheer volume of people I know who have faced the full ugliness of this beastly disease as they watched it chew through the people they love. I thought of all the other patients I would see every few weeks in the infusion center taking treatment—witnessing not only the deterioration of their bodies, but seeing the hopelessness in their eyes. I thought of all those who went through life without a father, a mother, a sibling, a spouse because this snake called cancer dragged them away.

Gone. So many people who were gone. So many loved ones: gone.

And yet there I was—still alive. Not because I had stronger faith or more prayers than others. Not because I was a better father, sibling, husband, son, friend, or colleague. Not because I was kinder, smarter, stronger, mentally tougher, funnier, or a better dancer. I didn't understand why. I certainly didn't feel worthy.

I was told that plenty of cancer patients struggle with the question "why me" when faced with the diagnosis. I had wrestled with that question somewhat after my diagnosis largely because it didn't feel fair to my family, but I also didn't think the disease seemed fitting for anyone. But that question—that emotion—now hung around my neck like an anchor carrying me to the bottom of a dark sea.

I pretended to be happy. I knew that I *should* be happy. I even went out the weekend after the news with my siblings to watch some local bands. I danced. I smiled. I laughed. I said all the right things to others who celebrated with me. After all, I knew that others deserved the celebration. Those who had lost others. Those who prayed for me. Those who loved me. They all deserved a happy ending. A smile and toast is what seemed appropriate. Isn't that what the world needs? So, I played the part.

But inside I felt like I was rotting. I felt so, so sad.

I was thankful for life. I was fortunate to escape—at least for the moment—the fire that had surrounded and engulfed my home and the homes of so many others. But I could not forget—nor did I want to forget—that there were so many who had been burned to death and so many still trapped inside.

Gone. I wanted all of this—the disease, suffering, sadness—gone. Not just for me, but everyone.

What gave me peace was reminding myself that the despair I felt was better than numbness. Life is about each new day. My time here simply wasn't done. I had more to give. I could honor those who had gone before me and those who still stood here with me—not only by remembering them—but by carrying on the qualities I admired in them the most: the sense of humor from a grandpa I never met; the drive and joy from a friend who persevered after losing his dad when he was only five years old; the hearty laugh from a nephew taken too soon; the wisdom and strength of my father who gave me agency; the unconditional love of my mother; the guidance of a mentor who taught me the power of whistling each day; the dedication and sacrifice of the doctors, nurses, and health care workers who cared for me—not just treated me, but really cared for me; and the love and kindness from friends, family, and strangers who stood with me through some of my darkest days and carried me when I needed it.

These—and so many others—are people who I would remember. Their lessons are the ones I would share. I would follow *their* example and spread *their* message. They taught me that life is about laughter, learning, and love. And, they are proof that we may pass from this life, but we are never gone.

CHAPTER 25:

BORROWED TIME

Life Lesson: *Not only does cancer erode a body. It floods a home.*

LIFE IS MESSY, FRAGILE, AND impermanent—like a sandcastle that stands at the edge of a shore. With each passing hour, a rising tide claws at its base, causing the structure to slowly crumble. We all fall eventually.

I completed a total of twelve chemotherapy treatments and thirty-two immunotherapy treatments. At least, that's what I've been told. I lost track. Treatment had become part of my schedule. I showed up for my appointments, worked on my laptop, felt the poke of a needle in my chest, repeated my name and date of birth for the nurses (a precautionary step they take to ensure they are giving the correct patient the proper medicine), watched my miracle bag of medicine (Pembrolizumab) be hung on the IV pole, waited for the liquid in the bag to slowly empty into my chest, drove home, and continued with my day as if I had stepped away to get a haircut.

My long-term prognosis remains uncertain. But, that is true of everyone. To paraphrase Dr. Helft, most people live under the illusion that they will live a long time. We are all facing death. I simply have more information than most. I know that I am on borrowed time. My most recent PET/CT scan showed increased activity throughout my lymph nodes and throughout my body with the blunt conclusion: *Overall findings are consistent with disease progression.*

When people ask how I am doing, I really don't know what to say. I usually reply saying, "I feel great." At least for now, it is the truth. I have few side effects from the treatment and I feel strong mentally, physically, and emotionally. However, it remains difficult to celebrate—not only because of the pain and anguish I continue to feel for others who faced a different fate, but because my family and I still don't know what lurks ahead for us. When others use words like "cured" or "behind you," we tighten—feeling like it might awaken the forces of nature, summoning the final crushing wave to our shores.

I remain deeply thankful for each new day. I can't honestly say each new sunrise looks more vibrant and the voices of birds are more beautiful, but I am deeply appreciative to continue being a husband, sibling, son, coworker, friend, and most importantly, a dad, for at least a little longer. I have savored watching Lizzie play soccer and seeing Anna Mae cheer and perform in the show choir. I am thankful to be there when they need help with schoolwork, to listen to some struggles they are having with a friend, laugh at Lizzie dressed like a Sumo wrestler during Halloween, teach Anna Mae to drive, watch them solve my clues and riddles to locate their Easter eggs, and squirt them with water on the last day of school.

On one of those glorious normal days, I sat down at my computer to continue writing. Anna Mae had asked to borrow my computer for a moment to print a paper for her freshman English class. She walked away, forgetting to close what she had open. On the screen was a poem she had written, a reminder that cancer impacts more than just the person with the diagnosis; it rattles an entire family. And, I realized that despite all the lessons I wanted to create *for* Anna Mae and Lizzie, I was still learning *from* them.

The Diagnosis
by Anna Mae Fischer

I remember the day,
the time,
specifically what I was doing,
I remember your face,
the grave disappointment.
I remember the conversation,
as if it had been in slow motion,
I remember the moment I thought my heart might have just stopped.
I covered my heartache with words of denial.
I concealed my fear with a big fake smile.
I felt alone, as though I had to keep it a secret.
I don't remember the details, life just felt different.
At the end of the day, you all broke to crumbles.
I didn't want more attention, so I tried to stay humble.
"I'm not the only one" I repeated to myself, daily.

Though I cried way too much, like a sad, hungry baby.

I tried to be strong, so I lied to myself.

And I ignored any updates related to your health.

The worst thing of all was seeing you cry,

It brought me so much pain, like salt in the eyes.

I explained to my best friend what was wrong,

but I couldn't take another "Try to stay strong."

When I said the word, I felt my guts churning,

tears raining down my face, my cheeks burning.

It took cousins, parents, sisters, and brothers,

and each year it takes six hundred thousand others.

Bringing so many people fear and sadness,

the dread to hear the incurable diagnosis.

It's unpredictable, so many questions, but no answer.

So much heartbreak that comes with the word "cancer."

Cancer had brought our entire family sadness, fear, anxiety, and suffering. It has been an unforgiving reminder that all our sandcastles eventually will return to the sea. But, it's also taught our family that it's not how quickly our life crumbles that matters most; it's the love and joy we share from building it and our appreciation of its beauty in the short time it lasts.

EPILOGUE

I'M NOT EXACTLY SURE HOW many more chapters in my life remain. None of us do.

My last round of immunotherapy was in September 2020. I continued to have CT scans every three months and another annual endoscopy/colonoscopy in August 2021. Although the CT scans continued to show growth and increased activity in my lymph nodes, the endoscopy/colonoscopy procedure did not find any malignant tumors. I continued to feel healthy and clung to normalcy.

One weekend in October 2021, after having a headache for a few days, I started having difficulty moving my left hand. Basic tasks like typing or reaching for the turn signal in my car suddenly became difficult. Since I had bumped my head a few days prior, I was concerned I might have a concussion. That weekend we found ourselves in a local ER. After we arrived, I informed the on-call doctor of my symptoms. He ordered a CT scan of my brain, which I assumed was standard procedure for anyone with a possible concussion. After completing the scan, we waited patiently in one of the hospital rooms for my results. Suddenly, the doctor entered the room, quietly stood for a moment, sympathetically looked me in the eye, and muttered, "Your CT scan shows what appears to be a large tumor on the right hemisphere of your brain."

His words, along with the indisputable image of a mass on my brain, crushed us like a tidal wave crashing to the shore. We sat in silence as he continued to explain the size and location of the tumor and our next steps, which included being immediately transferred by ambulance to IU Health Methodist Hospital in Indianapolis, who would evaluate me for possible brain surgery as quickly as possible. With each word he uttered, all my hopes of putting cancer behind my family and me disappeared like the grains of sand from a flattened sandcastle dispersing into the sea.

Three days later, two neurosurgeons removed my tumor. The pathology report of the brain tumor confirmed what was expected: the tumor was the same type of metastatic cancer originally found in my stomach. Because my lymph nodes continued to show increased activity, shortly after the neurosurgery team completed their work, another surgical team removed another one of my lymph nodes in my groin to also analyze it further. Both surgeries went well. However, this time the pathology report on my lymph node revealed two additional forms of cancer: Clinical stage IIIA diffuse large B-cell lymphoma and follicular lymphoma. My battle was not (and is not) over.

. . .

When I think of the impermanence of our human life, I often think of the Tibetan Buddhist monk tradition of creating beautiful art with colored sand. The math nerd in me is impressed by the complex geometry and precise symmetry used in the creation of the sand mandalas, as they are called. At its surface, grains of sand are shaped into carefully arranged geometric shapes with brilliant colors that, when complete, look like an image one might see in a kaleidoscope. However, to Tibetan Buddhists, the sand mandalas are much more than a fusion of mathematics and art. They often contain 722 deities portrayed within the mandala holding deep symbolic meaning and spiritual significance. The very act of creating the mandala is believed to be sacred, and monks train for years before they are allowed to create them in public.

The mandala often looks like a flattened or two-dimensional palace with four entryways into the palace. Each entryway represents one of the four states of mind, also known as the "Four Immeasurables" of Buddhism: loving kindness, compassion, altruistic joy, and equanimity. Buddhists don't think of these as simple emotions; each state requires deep meditation, intentional experiences, and a fundamental shift in the way one perceives oneself and others. Other parts of the mandala represent ignorance, anger, and lust—which Buddhists believe must be overcome in order to reach true enlightenment.

The mandala is collaboratively made by a small group of monks, with typically three or four monks working on it for several weeks. After it is completed, there is a brief ceremony and short time for public viewing. Then the beautiful mandala is swiftly destroyed and swept away with water—returning to the earth.

And so it is with my life and all our lives. Our time here is delicate, sacred, and fleeting. We are born and continue to slowly grow—collecting experiences, relationships, and memories along the way, but eventually all our time comes to an end. Although we may not be given a choice on the timing and nature of our death, we are given a choice on how we live. As powerful as anger, ignorance, and lust may be, they are no match for laughter, learning, and love.

ACKNOWLEDGMENTS

THERE IS NOTHING MORE PRECIOUS than our time. How we choose to spend our time is the most difficult and important decision we make each day. Writing a book takes time. Telling my story meant others sacrificed—especially my family. I would ignore or rush through family chores and family time together so I could capture the thoughts hanging in my head. Instead of crawling in bed at night with Tonya, I would disappear into my office to pour out my thoughts. Even when I couldn't explain why I needed to write, they understood. They didn't just allow it. They encouraged it. Tonya would read and edit my work and continued to be our family's rock when everything else surrounding us was shattering to pieces. Anna Mae and Lizzie were my biggest fans. They were my motivation to start the book, my inspiration to want to keep writing, and my primary audience with each word I wrote.

My editor, Kristen Hamilton, remained an honest and critical eye to my work. She helped me find and tell my story without changing my voice. She sniffed out when I was mollifying my emotions and challenged me to be honest with my readers and, more importantly, with myself. My book designer, Travis Hasenour, was able to take an abstract concept, like "please represent impermanence," and turned it into a work of art.

The support I received from family, friends, and complete strangers made me want to not only continue writing, but continue living. So many believed in me even when I didn't believe in myself. I will forever be grateful for all the love, support, and prayers I received.

To everyone who has helped me tell and live my story, thank you.

APPENDIX

A QUICK GUIDE TO CONVERTING your bucket list to a sand bucket list.

BUCKET LIST ITEMS	SAND BUCKET LIST ITEMS
Instead of focusing so much on doing these once...	*Consider doing these regularly and/or fully.*
Run a marathon.	Take a walk each day.
Bungee jump.	Fall in love.
Shoot a wild animal.	Have a squirt gun fight.
Visit the Amazon jungle.	Play tag on a jungle gym.
Travel to every continent.	Visit every nursing home in your area.
Go on a safari trip.	Go through a cornfield maze.
Backpack in the mountains.	Give someone a piggy-back ride.
Scuba dive in the Great Barrier Reef.	Play Marco Polo in a pool.
Experience zero gravity.	Experience equanimity with yoga.
Dogsled through the Alaskan Forest.	Adopt a pet from an animal shelter.
Get a tattoo.	Give blood.
Run with the bulls in Spain.	Pet a cow.
Rappel down a waterfall.	Go down a water slide.
Eat a tarantula.	Feed others at a food bank.
Stay at an all-inclusive resort.	Go camping.

ABOUT THE AUTHOR

BRAD LIVES WITH HIS WIFE and two daughters in Brownsburg, Indiana. He has been a high school math teacher, school district technology director, educational technology consultant, and data analytics leader. This is his debut book. When faced with stage 4 stomach cancer, writing became a connection to his past, therapy to make sense of his present, and a voice to his daughters' future.

Made in the USA
Middletown, DE
14 March 2023

26757599R00139